PENGUIN BOOKS

SEXWORDS

Jane Mills was born in London in 1948. After graduating from the University of Kent she was researcher on the official biography of Sir Winston Churchill and then political research assistant to Sir Harold Wilson. In 1973 she began her career as a documentary film-maker at Granada Television, eventually becoming Series Producer of Central TV's 'Science in Society' film-series. As an independent film-maker her films include *Yilmaz Guney: His Life, His Films* (C4) and *Rape: That's Entertainment?* (Omnibus, BBC1). Her interest in sex education led her to working with teenagers, their parents and teachers on the subject, and to writing *Make It Happy, Make It Safe* (Penguin, 1980), winner of *The Times Educational Supplement* Senior Information Book Award. She has also presented a weekly sex phone-in programme for Manchester's Piccadilly Radio, made the home-video *Learning to Love*, and contributed to *Sex Exposed: Sexuality and the Pornography Debate*. She has been Secretary of the Sexual Law Reform Society and the Defence of Literature and Arts Society, and a guest 'Agony Aunt' for several publications and radio stations. She is currently an Executive Committee member of the Edinburgh International Television Festival (of which she was the founder-director) and Head of Documentary at the Northern Media School at Sheffield Hallam University. Her other books are *Turkey: Torture and Political Persecution*, *Womanwords*, and *The Bloomsbury Guide to Erotic Literature*.

JANE MILLS

SEXWORDS

PENGUIN BOOKS

For Jessie, with all my love

PENGUIN BOOKS

Published by the Penguin Group
Penguin Books Ltd, 27 Wrights Lane, London W8 5TZ, England
Penguin Books USA Inc., 375 Hudson Street, New York, New York 10014, USA
Penguin Books Australia Ltd, Ringwood, Victoria, Australia
Penguin Books Canada Ltd, 10 Alcorn Avenue, Toronto, Ontario, Canada M4V 3B2
Penguin Books (NZ) Ltd, 182–190 Wairau Road, Auckland 10, New Zealand

Penguin Books Ltd, Registered Offices: Harmondsworth, Middlesex, England

First published 1993
10 9 8 7 6 5 4 3 2 1

Typeset by Datix International Limited, Bungay, Suffolk
Printed in England by Clays Ltd, St Ives plc
Set in 10/13 Monophoto Janson

Contents

Acknowledgements

As ever, my friends provided me with exactly the support system I needed to write this book. Special thanks to the following who between them gave me words, sources, ideas, advice, and corrections: Carol Akillian; Bill Anderson; Ruth Bundey; Julie Clarke; Sira Dermen; Bernie Enlander; Sandra Ferguson; Susie Figgis; Margaret Ford; Anna Gardiner; Dee Dee Glass; Caroline Glenny; Jonathon Green; Sarah Grigor; Chris Hamilton; Gill Lenderyou; Kathy Lette; Denis MacShane; Margaret Mulvihill; Lucy Neville; Richard Neville; Brian O'Kill; Katey Owen; Luisa Passerini; Peter Pringle; Geoffrey Robertson; Michael Rubinstein; Daniel Steel; Elaine Steel; Anne Schick; Liz Stoll; Dr Peter L. Thomas; Sharon Tracey; Arturo Varchekever; Margaret Walters. Those who read and criticized the manuscript in its various stages were the most long-suffering and special thanks are due to them. Thanks, also, to Rosemary Stones who had the idea for this book in the first place, and to Margaret Bluman, a truly understanding editor.

Above all, I would like to give my love and thanks to Charles Onion, my tireless researcher. A stern critic and a best friend, without him I wouldn't have had anything like the fun.

Introduction

Most people at some time or other find themselves in a situation where they're talking about sex but can't confess they don't know the meaning of a certain word. Or they pretend to laugh at a rude joke, not daring to admit they don't have the slightest idea what's so funny. They then look up the word in their standard dictionary and get no help at all – the definitions often contain even more words they don't understand. And if they do dare ask someone, they either get an embarrassed look or find that person doesn't know either.

This book should help. You'll find the technical, anatomical and medical terms as well as a lot of the slang. Some people may find the slang words shocking. But it's no good pretending that we need to know only the formal language – not many people talk like a biology textbook. And biology never feels as if it has much to do with our emotions. When it's good, sex is not just about how to put which parts of our bodies where. Although we may need to know this, we also need to relate this information to how we feel – about ourselves and about our partner. Putting words to our feelings isn't always easy, but it's usually a good idea to try. It's also a good idea to use the same language as the person you're trying to relate to.

Included in the definitions in this book are snippets of information about the history of the various words used by lovers, doctors, writers and anyone else who writes, talks or sings about sex and love. No one absolutely needs to know the history of a word in order to tell someone that they fancy or love them. But words are fascinating things – they can give pleasure and they can cause pain. Whoever wrote 'Sticks and stones can break my bones but words can never hurt me' didn't know what they were talking about. Knowing the history of a word may just give you a bit of historical knowledge or may explain why you do or don't think a certain word should be used. It may also help you understand what you're really feeling. In the case of a doctor or someone who is trying to persuade or force you to do something you don't want to do, it can be really useful to understand what they mean.

Some people think that ignorance is bliss and that knowledge destroys innocence. They're the sort who believe a book such as this puts ideas into the heads of young people. But adults have to face up to the fact that young people grow up. This is often when the young person is ready for it but not always when their parents are ready. It may well be that those who apparently grow up too soon do so precisely because they're ignorant and have no one to turn to when they want their questions answered.

A note on how to use this book. There are entries for over 500 words or terms, all connected to some aspect of sex, sexuality and love. If there's a particular word for which there doesn't seem to be an entry, take the nearest one that's spelled similarly or that you think has some connection with a topic and, without too much effort, you'll find the word and the meaning you were looking for. All words in small capitals within each entry have their own separate entry. Because this book is about words as well as sex there's a glossary at the end which explains some of the terms used by language experts.

If you come across a word or sexual practice which you think is obscene, rude or just not on, remember this extract from the novel *Forever* by Judy Blume, in which seventeen-year-old Kath is being pestered by her ten-year-old sister, Jamie, who asks:

'What were you two doing in your bedroom?'
'Nothing . . . Michael just wanted to see it.'
'Come on, Kath . . . I won't tell anybody.'
'There's nothing to tell.'
'I know all about sex.'
'Congratulations!'
'Were you fucking?'
'Jamie!'
'That's not a bad word . . . hate and war are bad words but fuck isn't.'
'I never said it was.'

'So were you?'

'No . . . I wasn't . . . but even if I was I wouldn't tell you.'

'Why not?'

'Because it's none of your damn business . . . that's why.'

'Oh wow . . .' she said, clucking her tongue, 'Your generation is so hung-up about sex.'

Jane Mills
London, 1992

A

abortion

This comes from the Latin word meaning 'to miscarry'. While a MISCARRIAGE happens naturally or spontaneously, abortion is generally used to refer to a pregnancy which is ended by a doctor.

The whole subject of abortion is very controversial. Some people believe every child should be a wanted child and that abortion should be available on demand to any girl or woman who needs one. Others are very opposed (even when the 'baby' is an EMBRYO) and would like abortion to be illegal or very much more difficult to obtain (see RIGHT TO LIFE).

The law on abortion varies from country to country and, in the USA, from state to state. In the UK, for example, it's possible to get an abortion up to the twenty-fourth week of pregnancy. A girl under the age of sixteen needs the permission of her parents, guardians or social worker if she is in care.

Abortion is illegal in Northern Ireland and in the Republic of Ireland (this has recently become a very contentious issue in these countries), but there are various FAMILY PLANNING clinics, pregnancy advisory services and well-woman clinics that may be able to arrange an abortion in England.

One of the good things about making abortion legal is that it means girls and women with an unwanted pregnancy aren't forced to go for a dangerous, illegal 'backstreet abortion' performed by an unqualified person.

A teenager who thinks she may be PREGNANT should get expert medical advice as soon as possible and not wait in the hope that her next period will come. If she doesn't feel she can tell her family doctor she should contact a PREGNANCY ADVISORY SERVICE. In the first three to five days after unprotected sex the morning-after birth-control method (the PILL or IUD) can be given before anyone can even know if they're definitely pregnant. See also RU 486.

During the first two weeks some doctors will perform a simple procedure, known as menstrual extraction, to empty out the contents of the WOMB. In the USA this is known as a 'lunch-time' abortion because it takes so little time.

For the first twelve weeks, the most common method is called vacuum aspiration, which takes only a few minutes. It is done under a local or a general anaesthetic. A very slim tube is inserted up the VAGINA through the CERVIX into the womb. The other end has a suction machine attached to it which draws out the contents of the womb.

In the middle stages of pregnancy minor operations such as a DILATATION AND CURETTAGE (D & C) or DILATATION AND EVACUATION (D & E) will probably be given. The cervix is stretched and the contents of the womb are gently scraped or drawn out. This is almost always done under a general anaesthetic and will probably require an overnight stay in hospital.

After sixteen weeks an induced abortion may have to be given. This can be traumatic because the girl or woman has to go through labour and childbirth. After twenty weeks there is a chance that the FOETUS will be alive, although it probably won't survive until it is about twenty–six weeks.

Although most women recover very quickly, abortions aren't easy things to go through. And it's seldom an easy decision to take. Even if she really didn't want to continue with the pregnancy (it may just be that her CONTRACEPTION failed but that at another time or with the right partner she would like to have a child), most girls and women (and their partners) feel sad afterwards and need some emotional support either from friends or from professional counsellors.

abuse

From a Latin word meaning 'to misuse', to abuse someone means to treat them insultingly, cruelly or violently. In a sexual sense, abuse usually refers to CHILD SEXUAL ABUSE (the sexual exploitation of a child by an adult), INCEST (the sexual abuse of a young person by a close member of her or his family) or RAPE (forcing someone to have SEXUAL INTERCOURSE against their will).

There are other ways in which people are sexually abused. Sexual HARASSMENT, FLASHING, OBSCENE PHONE CALLS, VOYEURISM (peeping Toms), WOLF-WHISTLES or anything which involves one person imposing her or his sexual demands on another and treating them like a SEX OBJECT, are all forms of abuse. Putting pressure on someone to have sex when they don't want to is a form of bullying and of exerting power.

Simply saying 'no' to someone who is abusing you is never easy. They may be someone you know. Talk to someone you trust to see if you can work out how not to be alone with the person who abuses you.

If you've been abused, you may need professional COUNSELLING to help to sort out your feelings. It's never the fault of the person being abused – no one ever asks, secretly desires or deserves to be maltreated or treated unjustly.

AC/DC
This is slang for a BISEXUAL, someone who is sexually attracted to both women and men. AC/DC is borrowed from the electrical term which stands for alternating current and direct current – suggesting 'first this way, then the other way'.

adolescence (add-oll-*ess*-ence)
From the Latin word meaning 'to grow up', adolescence is the period in everyone's life after PUBERTY and before adulthood, usually our early teens.

Adolescence can feel like hell. This is partly because our bodies start producing HORMONES which determine the development of what are called the 'secondary sex characteristics'. For girls these are BREASTS, larger vaginal lips (LABIA), PUBIC HAIR and underarm hair. For boys they are a larger, longer PENIS, voice-breaking and body hair (pubic, underarm and facial). These hormones eventually settle down, but at first they're produced at an irregular rate, and this can play havoc with emotions as well as causing pimples.

The physical changes taking place often make us feel self-conscious and awkward, and most adolescents have mixed feelings about growing up and becoming responsible for themselves. And it often takes adults, especially parents, a bit of time to realize that their teenage children are no longer children.

adultery

From the Latin word meaning 'to DEBAUCH, corrupt', adultery means SEXUAL INTERCOURSE between a married person and someone who isn't their husband or wife. Most religions see adultery as a sin. The seventh of the Ten Commandments that Moses brought down from Mount Sinai states clearly, 'Thou shalt not commit adultery' (Exodus 20:14). Muslims share this view. In almost all countries adultery is grounds for divorce but is no longer a criminal offence.

Historically, an adulterous wife was considered worse than an adulterous husband. In ancient Hebrew times a wife was expected to share her husband with one or more secondary wives or CONCUBINES (see POLYGAMY) but could be stoned to death if she took a lover. Inheritance laws made it more acceptable for a man to commit adultery than for a woman; men needed to be certain that they were the father of their wife's child. In England it wasn't until 1923 that women won the equal right to divorce their husband on the grounds that he had committed adultery. Male pride and a belief that men 'owned' their wives also played a large part – and still do in some cases.

afterplay

Most sex manuals mention FOREPLAY, but few ever mention any sort of afterplay. After a male has an ORGASM, he often feels completely satisfied. After a female has COME, she usually still feels quite 'high' and is often able to come again. If she comes several times, this is called a multiple orgasm. Each orgasm won't necessarily be as intense as the first, although the second or third can sometimes be the best. Few women have several orgasms each time, but it is possible for some to reach a peak of excitement again more quickly than their male partners. And even if a woman doesn't feel like another orgasm, her body differs from a man's in that she takes more time to 'come down' afterwards. A man who simply rolls over and goes to sleep immediately after he's come will probably leave his female partner feeling abandoned and unsatisfied.

It's good sexual manners – as well as more loving – for each partner to find out what the other likes. Some stroking and cuddling (or whatever feels good) after you've had your orgasm is one way of showing your feelings and is every bit as important as foreplay.

age of consent

Legally, young people are not considered capable of giving their consent to SEXUAL INTERCOURSE until they reach a certain age, known as the age of consent. This applies only to girls and HOMO-SEXUAL boys and varies from country to country. In the UK the age of consent is sixteen for girls and twenty-one for gays. In the USA the age of consent for girls is twelve in some states and eighteen in others and also varies for male homosexuals. There is no country which has an age of consent for a LESBIAN girl.

In the UK, a male who has sex with a girl under the age of consent, even if she wanted to have sex, is guilty of having 'unlawful sexual intercourse'. This is illegal, but it's not considered to be as serious a crime as RAPE. The girl is not considered to have committed any crime, although she may find herself put into care if it's thought that she sleeps around (see PROMISCUITY). In the USA even if the girl wanted to have sex and knew what she was doing, the boy or man who has sex with a girl under the age of consent set by the state is guilty of STATUTORY RAPE. (See also LOLITA.)

Many people question these laws, which seem to be intended to protect the CHASTITY of girls but not of boys, are stricter for gays than they are for straights and make it a crime for a male to have sex even with a willing partner. Plenty of other laws exist which can protect a young person from sexual abuse. But, conversely, these laws may deter young people who are sexually active from going to clinics and doctors to get advice on BIRTH CONTROL. This may result in an unwanted PREGNANCY. Few doctors and no FAMILY PLANNING clinic (see also PREGNANCY ADVISORY SERVICES), which exist to help teenagers prevent unwanted pregnancies, would report a boy with an under-age girlfriend.

AID See ARTIFICIAL INSEMINATION BY DONOR.

AIDS

AIDS stands for Acquired Immune Deficiency Syndrome. 'Acquired' means something you're not born with and that you get later on in life. 'Immune' refers to the healthy body's immunity system (in the blood) which protects us from illness. 'Deficiency' means a lack – in this context it means the body's immune system lacks the ability to prevent infection. A 'syndrome' is a group of illnesses which identify a particular condition.

AIDS isn't one illness but a condition in which the person gets a variety of illnesses, most probably from a virus called HIV (Human Immunodeficiency Virus). This virus is present in the bodily fluids of an infected person – blood, SEMEN, URINE, FAECES (shit), secretions from the VAGINA, menstrual blood (see MENSTRUATION), breast milk and saliva.

Because AIDS is a condition resulting from the breakdown of the body's immune system caused by a virus, you can't 'catch' AIDS itself. It's not like a plague or a cold germ which you breathe in. The virus is very fragile, and outside the body it dies almost immediately. This means you can't get the virus (or AIDS) from touching someone who is infected, from a toilet seat or a swimming pool, from drinking out of the same cup or from using the same cooking utensils. Mosquitoes can't spread the virus either. It can spread only if any of the bodily fluids of an infected person enter the bloodstream of another person. Promiscuity (sleeping around) in itself doesn't cause AIDS, but the more partners you have, the more likely you are to come across someone with the virus.

Someone with the virus is said to be HIV-positive. They may remain apparently healthy for a number of years, showing no symptoms at all, or they may experience weight loss, bouts of sweating, a persistent cough and flu-like symptoms. As their immune system becomes increasingly unable to cope with infection they may develop AIDS-related complex (ARC). This usually means symptoms such as swollen lymph glands in the armpits or the back of the neck, certain skin infections, THRUSH in the mouth, diarrhoea and other general signs of ill-health.

Once someone has AIDS itself, they tend to get what are known as 'opportunistic infections'. These are diseases which take the opportunity provided by an inefficient immune system. These diseases can include a cancer called KAPOSI'S SARCOMA, pneumonia, infections of the intestine, various neurological disorders and several different types of tumour. Although a person with AIDS can live healthily for a long time, it is usually one of these serious opportunistic infections that eventually causes death.

Throughout the world the most common way for the virus to be spread is by SEXUAL INTERCOURSE, both vaginal and anal (see ANAL INTERCOURSE). For example, the semen of a man with HIV can get into the bloodstream of his partner by being absorbed either through the walls of her vagina or anus or through the tiny cuts and tears that sometimes happen inside the vagina or anus during lovemaking. If the virus is present in the natural secretions inside a woman's vagina, it can be absorbed through the delicate tissue in the tip of the penis. It is just possible, although unlikely, for the virus to be passed during ORAL SEX, when the mouth comes into contact with the penis or vagina.

Non-sexual ways for the virus to spread are from the mother to her baby during childbirth and by breast-feeding and among drug-users who share unsterilized needles. In the past some haemophiliacs (people with a rare blood disease who need regular blood transfusions) got the virus because the blood banks didn't know about HIV. All blood banks now test donors for HIV.

There is currently no cure for HIV or for AIDS. This means that prevention is extremely important. You can't tell just by looking at someone if they have the virus. Everyone, gay or straight, who has a sex life should take precautions and practise SAFER SEX.

AIDS is something you can live with for a fairly long time, so many people with this illness like to be known not as 'sufferers' or 'victims' but simply as a PLWA (Person Living With AIDS).

all the way

This slang term, mostly used by teenagers, means to have SEXUAL INTERCOURSE involving PENETRATION of the VAGINA or ANUS by a PENIS. The first time you go all the way you are said to have lost your VIRGINITY.

Expressions like this, and others such as 'making it' and 'getting there', make it sound as if sex has to be about full intercourse. SAFER SEX, however, has taught people that good sex doesn't have to mean penetration. You can give and receive sexual pleasure and satisfaction by doing with your partner a whole range of things that don't run a high risk of spreading the HIV virus (which can lead to AIDS) or of getting pregnant without going all the way.

amenorrhoea (amen-or-*rear*)

An 'a' at the beginning of a word often means 'without'; 'men' is short for 'mensis' which is Latin for 'month'; 'rrhoea' comes from the Latin verb 'to flow'. Put these three parts together and you get 'without the monthly flow'. Or, in other words, a girl's monthly PERIODS which are either totally absent or very infrequent.

MENSTRUATION (the technical term for periods) starts at PUBERTY, which usually occurs in a girl's early teens and finishes when a woman reaches MENOPAUSE, usually in her mid- to late forties. For the first year or so after they've started menstruating few girls experience very regular periods. But once their HORMONES are balanced, periods happen more or less every twenty-eight days, although few are absolutely regular.

A girl may stop menstruating for a variety of reasons – because she's pregnant, ill, has had an emotional shock or is undernourished. She may find her periods become irregular if she suffers from a mild eating disorder; they may stop completely if she suffers from an extreme eating disorder like anorexia nervosa or bulimia. It's not always a symptom of ill health – many girls in intensive sports training don't menstruate. But amenorrhoea can be a sign that she is not OVULATING every month, which may be due to a hormone imbalance. It's something that needs to be checked out with a doctor.

A girl whose periods are irregular will usually be fertile (see FERTILIZATION) but never knows when her period is going to happen. This can be inconvenient and very worrying. Her doctor will probably prescribe 'the PILL', used to prevent pregnancy, containing a combination of oestrogen and progestagen. The pill is a very convenient way of regulating periods. It can also be prescribed if she wants to avoid having a period at a crucial time – say, for an exam, race, field trip or holiday.

Coming off the pill can cause a mild bout of depression due to the change in hormone levels which occurs in the body.

If a woman has no periods at all ('primary amenorrhoea'), it may well mean she is infertile. This, again, can cause a lot of worry and must be discussed with a doctor if nothing has happened by her late teens. Blood tests may be necessary, and hormones (in pill form) may be used to check the functioning of the UTERUS. If there are no problems, a pill cycle may be prescribed. But if this doesn't work, there's little that can be done. If she wants to have a baby, she may respond well to hormone implantation.

Not being able to get pregnant doesn't mean that a girl should stop practising SAFER SEX by using a condom.

amyl nitrate See POPPER.

anaerobic vaginosis
'Anaerobic' means 'without air or oxygen'. This is a bacterial infection of the VAGINA, formerly called non-specific vaginitis, which may be a SEXUALLY TRANSMITTED DISEASE. Symptoms include a watery, fishy-smelling vaginal discharge which is often worse after unprotected SEXUAL INTERCOURSE. Although males may show no symptoms, both partners should go for treatment to their doctor or to a SPECIAL CLINIC and use a CONDOM until it has been cured.

anal intercourse/anal sex
Also called BUGGERY and SODOMY, anal sex involves the penetration

of the PENIS through the ANUS, which is the entry to the rectum or back passage.

Anal sex is definitely not a feature of SAFER SEX. The anus is normally a fairly tight ring of muscle, and the walls of the rectum are very fragile. This means that small cuts and tears are likely to occur when an erect penis is pushed in (the penis may suffer a few tears too). This makes it very easy for any bodily fluids infected with HIV (semen, faeces or blood) to enter the partner's bloodstream.

Any couple who feel they must have anal sex should always use some LUBRICANT, such as KY jelly, as well as a lubricated CONDOM. There are some extra thick, and therefore safer, condoms made just for this purpose. A SPERMICIDE which destroys HIV should also be used. But no condom is guaranteed to be burst-proof.

Many people assume that all male HOMOSEXUALS have anal intercourse. They don't. For many, making love means having an orgasm by KISSING, stroking and MASTURBATING each other. Many gays who once enjoyed anal sex have learned how to make love by practising safer sex a lot sooner than most HETEROSEXUALS and no longer have anal sex, or never have it, without a lubricated condom and a spermicide.

Although many lovers, both GAY and STRAIGHT, enjoy anal intercourse, to some people the idea can seem very unpleasant, even frightening. This is understandable because most of us think of our anus only in terms of FAECES, or shit as it is commonly called. But most people, if they're honest, will admit that they feel some pleasure when they have a bowel movement.

Like so many things about sex, there are people who get very uptight about what others do in the privacy of their own bedrooms. In some countries anal intercourse is actually illegal – even between a married couple. It can be grounds for divorce if a husband forces his wife to have anal sex against her will (see ABUSE).

androgyny (an-*droj*-jenny)
An androgyne is someone with both female and male characteristics. The word comes from a combination of two Greek words – *andros* meaning male or man and *gyne* meaning female or woman. In Greek

mythology the androgyne was a sexually alluring creature with BREASTS and a PENIS.

In extremely rare cases babies are born with this condition – they may be helped by psychosexual counsellors and by hormones when they're older. Most often, however, androgyny is a matter of style or looks. The word 'androgynous' is used to refer to someone who seems to be neither distinctly female nor male; it may be a question of fashion or because he or she is BISEXUAL and is attracted to both sexes. Some actors and pop stars deliberately adopt an androgynous look – perhaps to appeal to both females and males in their audiences, perhaps because they 'swing both ways' as a bisexual preference is sometimes known.

anus (*ayn*-uss)

Anus is a Latin word for the opening to the rectum, or back passage, at the end of the digestive tract through which FAECES is pushed out. It is a tight ring of muscle which relaxes during sex to allow in a finger or a PENIS during ANAL SEX.

Slang for the anus includes bum hole, arse hole, asshole, exhaust pipe, back garden, back hole, backeye, brown-eye, dinger, blot, poop chute, etc. A favourite American term in the 1950s was keister or keester. This was first used by criminals to refer to the anus as a safe place to hide stolen goods. Keister later also came to be general slang for the human bottom, for the back pockets in a pair of trousers and for a safe or strong-box.

aphrodisiac (afro-*diz*-ee-ak)

Also called a love potion, this is something which supposedly makes you feel sexy. It gets its name from Aphrodite, the ancient Greek goddess of love.

Over the years a huge number of foods have been thought to make people feel sexually excited – from mushrooms and tomatoes (once called love apples) to powdered rhino horn and most shellfish. Spanish fly, made from the remains of the *Cantharis visicatoria* beetle, is very dangerous and can be fatal – the Marquis de Sade was once jailed for administering Spanish fly to some PROSTITUTES. But as an aphrodisiac it is no more effective than a potato, which was also once seriously believed to be capable of making people feel sexy.

There is no medical evidence to support the view that a substance can make you sexually potent. Some sex shops sell preparations to gullible people, claiming them to have aphrodisiac qualities. Like most sex toys and aids, the shop and the manufacturer make a lot of profit – but you may get some fun from them.

'Aphrodisiac' now has a wider sense and is used for anything that turns anyone on. When Henry Kissinger, the US Secretary of State in the 1970s, was asked how such a plain-looking man managed to pull so many young, attractive women, he is said to have replied, 'Power is the ultimate aphrodisiac.'

ARC (AIDS-related complex) See AIDS.

areola (arr-ee-*oh*-la)
The areola is the coloured ring of skin tissue around the NIPPLE on each BREAST. The word comes from the Latin for a 'small open space' – from which we also get the word 'area'.

In children the areola is a pale, pinkish colour. It goes brownish during PUBERTY. When a woman is pregnant her areola usually goes much darker, sometimes almost black, and often stays darker after the baby is born.

around the world
This is a phrase often used by PROSTITUTES when advertising their services. It means KISSING your partner's body all over, including their PENIS and TESTICLES or VAGINA as well as their ANUS. (See also ORAL SEX.)

arousal
Kissing, stroking, and love-talk are ways of getting your partner sexually aroused. See FOREPLAY.

arse/ass
The word 'arse' (from the Greek word meaning TAIL) was a totally

acceptable word or Standard English (see Glossary) term for the buttocks until the seventeenth century, when it was considered too rude for polite conversation. From then until the 1930s it was usually printed as 'ar--' or 'a--e'. It's possible that the American spelling and pronunciation of it as 'ass' may have sounded more polite (see EUPHEMISM in the Glossary). It was probably also influenced by the idea that a 'bum', as tramps are called in America – where a tramp means a sexually PROMISCUOUS woman – is as stupid as a donkey, which is a type of ass; the term 'silly ass' can therefore have two meanings (see DOUBLE ENTENDRE in the Glossary). Bum, meaning backside, was also Standard English until around the end of the eighteenth century.

Also in America, perhaps in order not to use the word CUNT, arse or ass slipped around the female body and came to mean the VAGINA. FANNY slipped around the other way: it started off as slang for the vagina and ended up in America as a more polite term for a bottom. The insulting term a BIT or 'piece of arse/ass' means a female who is either sexually desirable (to a male) or one who is considered to be sexually available (see SEX OBJECT). It is not a flattering term to any woman who believes that she is a lot more than her backside or her vagina. An 'arse/ass man' is slang for a male who is attracted chiefly to a woman's buttocks and for a HETEROSEXUAL male who is obsessed by having or thinking about sex. In the USA this term, and sometimes 'ass QUEEN', is also used for a male HOMOSEXUAL. This assumes, wrongly, that all GAYS practise ANAL SEX.

artificial insemination by donor (AID)

In this context artificial means 'not natural', in the sense of being by a method other than SEXUAL INTERCOURSE. Insemination means 'introduce SEMEN into', based on the Latin word for a seed. A donor is a 'giver of a gift', from the Latin verb for 'to give', from which we also get the word 'donation'.

A woman who is unable to get pregnant because her husband or partner is STERILE, or perhaps because she is a single woman or a LESBIAN and has no wish to have sexual intercourse, can have some SPERM placed inside her WOMB by a medically trained person. The donor's sperm is obtained from a SPERM BANK and remains completely anonymous.

The term 'virgin birth' is used when a woman who is inseminated in this way has never had sexual intercourse. It is a term more often used to describe the popular Christian belief that Mary, the mother of Jesus, was made pregnant by the Holy Spirit.

asexual

The 'a' part of this word means 'without', giving the meaning of non-sexual or lacking in sexual interest or activity. (See also PLATONIC.)

B

backstreet abortion See ABORTION.

bad

The word 'bad' can sometimes mean 'good'. And things that are thought to be good are sometimes called bad. A lot depends on who is using the word and who or what is being described. If a girl or woman is called bad, it usually means she's being accused of being IMMORAL or PROMISCUOUS. If a boy or man, on the other hand, puts it around a lot (another term for promiscuity) he gets called 'bad' and it means that he's greatly approved of. When Michael Jackson named his album *Bad* in the 1980s he probably thought that those who bought it would think he was good because he was sexy, although people with more traditional views thought he was a bad influence because he was sexy.

The word bad has a long history of being connected to sex. Its roots go back to the Old English word *baeddel*. This originally meant a person who had the characteristics of both sexes – known as a HERMAPHRODITE or ANDROGYNE. From this the word *badling* developed, which first meant a man who practised ANAL SEX and later came to mean an effeminate fellow or a womanish man. Another old word which developed from *baeddel* was *badde*, which was used at first to mean a male HOMOSEXUAL. It later came to mean something or someone who was defective or worthless which is how bad is mostly used today.

It wasn't until the twentieth century that bad began to be used in the sense that Michael Jackson used it – as sexy and therefore good. The tendency to use a word to mean its opposite probably started with Black American Jazz slang in the 1920s – so 'cool' can mean 'hot', and 'mean' can suggest something really terrific.

balanitis

'Balan' is Greek for acorn and is often found in medical words connected to the CLITORIS or the top part of the PENIS or GLANS, because the shape of both resembles an acorn. Balanitis is an inflammation of the clitoris or the glans of the penis (especially at the place where the FORESKIN is attached to the penis). The skin tissue often becomes swollen, tender and itchy and sometimes develops ulcerous sores and venereal WARTS. This infection can have a variety of causes. It may be the result of a blockage in the opening to the URETHRA in the tip of the penis, or of a fungus similar to the one that causes THRUSH, and it can also be a SEXUALLY TRANSMITTED DISEASE spread by ANAL SEX. Any one who thinks they may have balanitis should go to their doctor or to a SPECIAL CLINIC that deals with VENEREAL DISEASES, and use a CONDOM if they have SEXUAL INTERCOURSE, until they are cured.

ball/balls

The verb 'to ball' is slang for to have SEXUAL INTERCOURSE. The expression seems to have been invented in the USA in the 1950s and probably comes from the phrase 'to have a ball', which means to have a good time and originates from the Latin word for 'to dance'. It doesn't seem to have any connection with the term 'balls' as in the expression 'that's a load of (old) balls' meaning nonsense or rubbish, or 'he's got balls' meaning guts or courage. In both these cases balls refer to the TESTICLES. The word made legal history in the UK in 1929 when it was judged to be OBSCENE. In America, the word 'boloney' or 'baloney' has always been more popular as a slang term for nonsense or worthless talk. Boloney, however, comes from another part of the male anatomy; it's a word-play on the PENIS-shaped Bologna sausage.

A ball-buster or ball-breaker is an uncomplimentary term used mostly by males to refer to a woman who threatens a man's pride or masculinity in some way, because to destroy a man's testicles literally would CASTRATE him.

barren

If a girl or woman is barren it means she's STERILE and can't have children. It is the opposite of FERTILE.

Bartholin's gland (bar-*toll*-ins)

Caspar Bartholin II was a seventeenth-century Danish anatomist who discovered two glands at the entrance to the VAGINA which produce a wet secretion. He believed the purpose of this fluid was to make it easier for the PENIS to slide into the vagina during SEXUAL INTERCOURSE. It's since been discovered that these glands produce only very little secretion and probably too late to make much difference. In fact, the whole inner surface of the vaginal walls secrete a LUBRICATING fluid when a girl or woman is getting sexually aroused (see FOREPLAY).

bastard

A bastard is someone whose parents were not married when they were born, but it's most commonly used as a term of abuse. It's a medieval English word which probably comes from a French phrase *fils de bast* meaning either 'son of the pack-saddle' or 'son of the barn'. What this meant was that the mother had no idea who the father of her child was because she'd had SEXUAL INTERCOURSE with a passing traveller. In those days it didn't matter if a girl was illegitimate because inheritance laws meant that the family name and property was only passed down to the son. But it was essential for a husband to be absolutely sure that his wife gave birth to his own legitimate male children. ADULTERY laws are based on this notion.

To call someone a bastard could suggest you think they're illegitimate and that their mother is PROMISCUOUS. The phrase 'son of a BITCH' can also suggest bastard since female dogs, when they're on heat, will have sex with any passing dog in order to fall pregnant.

bat

Perhaps because they are rather mysterious animals, bats have never been much loved. There has been a connection in most people's minds between bats and ugly, morally suspect women since medieval times. Since the early 1600s when mainly old women were tortured and burned alive because they were popularly believed to have sex with the devil and fly at night on broomsticks, bat has been slang for a low WHORE, apparently because PROSTITUTES swoop down on prospective customers at dusk.

In the 1950s a good-conduct code drawn up by American television broadcasters picked out bat as one of the words that should never be used if it was applied to a woman. Today, the term 'old bat' usually means a girl or young woman who men find sexually unattractive or even repulsive.

baths

In the USA, if a GAY man goes to the baths, he isn't expecting a wash; he generally goes there to have sex with another HOMOSEXUAL. Baths would be the gay equivalent of MASSAGE PARLOURS for HETEROSEXUALS where the customers can drink, dance, watch BLUE MOVIES, have a sauna and maybe swim, and find a partner to have sex with in small cubicles.

bawdy

Bawdy means a mixture of 'boisterous' and 'humourously INDECENT'. The word may come from an Old French word meaning bold and merry. In the Middle Ages a bawd was a woman or man who acted as a go-between for two lovers. By the late sixteenth century it meant a PIMP or a female brothel-keeper (see MADAM). A BROTHEL is still sometimes called a bawdy house. Today, a bawd is an obsolescent (see Glossary) word for a PROSTITUTE. A piece of sexually suggestive, coarse or OBSCENE writing might still be called bawdy although it's more likely to be described as PORNOGRAPHIC.

beast with two backs

Also known as 'two-humped beast', this phrase appears in many different languages as a graphic description of a woman and a man making love. It was probably first used by the French writer, monk and doctor François Rabelais (1494–1533) in his famously BAWDY book *Gargantua*. In Shakespeare's *Othello*, Iago says to Brabantio:

'I am one, Sir, that comes to tell you your daughter and the Moor are now making the beast with two backs.'

beaver

This word is a slang term for the female GENITALS, perhaps because the hairy and usually dark shape of a woman's pubic area looks like a beaver when it's swimming. Or, more likely, because the triangle of PUBIC HAIR looks like a man's beard which has also been called a 'beaver' since the late nineteenth century. 'Beard' is also slang for the VULVA – both a man's beard and a woman's pubic hair surround lips (see LABIA) and 'bearded clam' is slang for the VAGINA. A 'beard-splitter' was once slang for a PENIS. 'Split-beaver' is the name given to PORNOGRAPHIC photographs of women which show the labia wide open, revealing the entrance to the VAGINA.

beefcake

This word was invented in the USA in the 1950s as the male version of CHEESECAKE. Beef and cheese both come from cows, but 'beefcake' refers to a man (or a picture of a man in a magazine) with sex appeal who shows off his muscles and good looks. 'Beef' has been slang for PENIS since the nineteenth century – although one hundred years earlier 'to be in a woman's beef' meant to have SEXUAL INTERCOURSE with a woman. In Shakespeare's time 'beef-brained' meant a complete idiot. A man described as a beefcake is rarely thought to have much intelligence.

bent

In English slang 'bent' can mean 'a male PERVERT'. In the USA it means 'a HOMOSEXUAL'. It seems to have been used originally as a term of abuse by HETEROSEXUALS (see HOMOPHOBIA) because the word was the opposite of STRAIGHT. Bent can also mean 'crooked', which is slang for 'criminal'. Until the late 1960s homosexuality between males was illegal in the UK and still is illegal in some American states.

berk

To call someone, usually a boy or man, a berk is a fairly harmless way of saying you think they're a bit silly, irritating, or not very good at what they're doing. Perhaps because they rhyme, the words berk and jerk are used in the same way. Jerk comes from 'jerk off' meaning to MASTURBATE. In fact, the word berk comes from another source altogether. It's short for Berkshire or Berkeley Hunt, which is rhyming slang (see Glossary) for CUNT.

bestiality

This means sexual relations between a person and an animal and is a criminal offence in most countries. It's been considered an 'unnatural practice' or an 'abomination' ever since humankind started writing laws about what type of sex was acceptable and what wasn't. The Old Testament makes it clear that bestiality is unacceptable: 'If a man lies with a beast, he shall be put to death; and you shall kill the beast. If a woman approaches any beast and lies with it, you shall kill the woman and the beast. (Leviticus 20:15–16).

Bestiality is rare in large urban communities but not infrequent in rural areas – perhaps because of the comparative lack of barriers between humans and animals. Psychologists use the term zoophilia, from the Greek word 'zoo' meaning 'animal' and 'philia' meaning 'lover of', and regard it as a psychosexual disorder or PERVERSION.

Many ancient myths and legends tell of half-human, half-animal beings born as the result of SEXUAL INTERCOURSE between a human and an animal. In reality this is completely impossible.

bigamy (*big*-ammee)

This is the crime of marrying someone when you're already married to someone else. The second marriage is called bigamous and is not legally recognized. The 'bi' comes from the Latin for twice and 'gamous' from the Greek meaning married (see also POLYGAMY).

bimbo

This is a young woman thought to be very stupid, sexy and a bit of a 'gold-digger'. It reinforces a widespread but groundless belief that an attractive woman cannot also be intelligent. The popular British newspapers fell upon the word with great gusto in the late 1980s when reporting a story about a couple of highly glamorous female models who were engaged in a legal dispute, referred to as the

'Battle of the Bimbos', about the theft of some private diaries which revealed a lot of sexy details.

Just before the First World War (1914–1918) the word 'bimbo' arrived in the USA shortened from the Italian word *bambino*, meaning little child or baby. It was used in an unflattering way to refer to a guy. Soon after this the meaning of the word widened and was used to mean anyone, female or male, who was unimportant. In the 1920s it was shortened to 'bim' and applied to any girl or woman, especially to a girlfriend – perhaps because they were seen to be less important than their boyfriend. In the nineteenth century 'bim' was British slang for a blow or punch with the fist and, by the early 1920s, for a strong or tough man.

By the 1930s a bimbo was a PROSTITUTE or a PROMISCUOUS woman. During the Second World War (1939–1945) American soldiers used the word to mean an Army recruit – someone who is not very highly regarded within the military.

In the late 1980s 'bimbette' was invented. At first it mostly referred to ADOLESCENT female pop-singers, but now it has largely replaced bimbo in common usage. The '-ette' is a suffix (see Glossary) borrowed from French, which in English often implies something that is female, small and of less value than the male version.

birth canal

Also called the birth passage, this is another word for the VAGINA since the baby is pushed out through it during childbirth.

birth control See CONTRACEPTION.

bisexual

A bisexual is a person – female or male – who is sexually attracted to both sexes. The same word can also mean someone who has the characteristics of both sexes (see HERMAPHRODITE, ANDROGYNE) although it's not often used in this sense. Scientific studies show that there are traces of the sexual organs of both sexes in each EMBRYO. Psychologists believe that most people are bisexual to some degree – part HOMOSEXUAL and part HETEROSEXUAL.

bit

Bit has been used since Victorian times as an informal term (see
COLLOQUIALISM in the Glossary) for a young woman or girl, especially
one regarded as a sex object. Since the formal definition of 'bit' is a small,
often unimportant, amount of something, it's not a flattering term. The
phrase 'to have a bit' is used mostly by men meaning to have SEXUAL
INTERCOURSE. A 'bit on the side' was once used only to describe a female
lover in an adulterous relationship. In the 1960s married women who
were unfaithful also began to use it of their male lovers (see ADULTERY).

Since the 1850s women have been called 'a bit' of the following:
black velvet, crumb, CUNT, ebony, fluff, grease, jam, muslin, mutton,
raspberry (perhaps a reference to a woman having her period), skirt,
soap, stuff, tripe, crackling and spare (from Adam's spare rib out of
which God made Eve).

bitch

When the word bitch, or *bicce* as it was originally spelled, first
entered the English language (around the beginning of the eleventh
century) it meant nothing more or less than a female dog. But during
the fifteenth century it began to be applied in a reproachful sense to
a woman, especially one who was thought to be LEWD. A hundred
years later it had become a very negative term meaning a WHORE.
In the twentieth century, to call a woman a bitch might suggest that
she is mean and nasty. When used as a verb, 'to bitch' means to talk
with malice, spite or selfishness. If a man is accused of being bitchy
there is a strong suggestion that he is EFFEMINATE.

Bitch has such strong, negative sexual implications that it has
almost become a swear word. Children are often taught to refer to 'a
girl dog' rather than use the correct term.

blow job

A blow job is slang for FELLATIO which comes from the Latin for 'to
suck'. It involves kissing, licking and sucking the PENIS. In the USA
a blow job also means CUNNILINGUS. How an activity which involves
sucking rather than blowing came to have this name is a mystery.
(See also ORAL SEX and SOIXANTE-NEUF).

blue balls/veiner

A blue veiner is a colloquial term (see Glossary) for a very stiff ERECTION from the main vein running along the length of the PENIS which shows particularly clearly at such times. For 'blue balls' see FRUSTRATION.

blue joke/movie

Blue has been used to describe something that was considered smutty or indecent since the 1830s, perhaps from the colour that PROSTITUTES were forced to wear to distinguish them from respectable women. 'To turn the air blue' means to curse or use obscene or blasphemous language. As a result, a PORNOGRAPHIC film became known as a 'blue movie', and a dirty joke as a 'blue' one.

bodice ripper

In the early twentieth century, women's romantic novels never used to mention sex. In the 1960s and '70s the heroines, who were always being seduced, were made love to more explicitly and the term 'bodice ripper' was coined to describe this type of fiction – these novels usually reflected the myth that women enjoy being treated roughly or even RAPED. In the 1980s female sexuality came out in the open and these books became known as BONK-busters or 'S&F', which stands for 'shopping and FUCKING'.

bollocks

This is another word for the TESTICLES which, until fairly recently, was spelt ballocks. It's a very old word which was Standard English up to about 1840, when it was considered too vulgar to be used in polite society. Like the word BALLS, bollocks is also used to mean nonsense or worthless talk. To get a bollocking means to be reprimanded or scolded and is a pun (see Glossary) on ball, meaning testicle, and bawl, meaning to be shouted at.

bondage

This is the term for sexual activity involving being tied down or having the hands and feet tied together. Someone who can only get sexual satisfaction in this way is said to be suffering from a psycho-sexual disorder, or PERVERSION, known as SADO-MASOCHISM.

PROSTITUTES sometimes advertise that they provide 'B&D' – this stands for 'bondage and discipline'. Discipline usually involves the use of whips and leather belts. A woman who disciplines her sexual partner like this is known as a dominatrix.

bonk

The verb to bonk, meaning SEXUAL INTERCOURSE, arrived on the scene in the mid-1980s. A 'BIMBO-bonker' is a man who has sexual intercourse with a young woman who has more sex appeal than brains. A 'bonk-buster', meaning a highly popular and successful novel with lots of sex in it, is a play on words from the term 'block-buster' (see BODICE RIPPER). 'Bonk journalism' was invented by the British newspaper, the *Guardian*, to describe a cross between an investigation into the sexual activities of famous people and PORNOGRAPHY.

Bonk is usually used lightly and with a sense of amusement; it's a way of saying FUCK without shocking anyone. Its origins are debatable. A likely theory is that it comes from the use of bonk, meaning to hit or tap something, probably invented because the word sounds like the noise made when you hit something. It started life as a public school-boy expression just after the First World War (1914–1918), possibly because of its similarity to the word 'bang' which soldiers used for gunshell noise. 'Bang' is also slang for fuck (see GANG-BANG). 'Shoot' is widely-used slang for EJACULATION.

A 'bonk on' has been slang for an ERECTION since the 1950s. The similar-sounding term 'stonk on' is also slang for an erection and was army slang during the Second World War (1939–1945) for a heavy artillery shelling as in 'giving 'em a stonk'.

boobs

Boobs or boobies are slang terms for women's BREASTS from the word 'bubbies' which was Standard English (see Glossary) until the late eighteenth century. Bubbies may come from the word 'bub', an old word which meant 'to drink', or possibly from the 'boo boo' sound a baby makes when it's hungry and wants some breast-milk (see ONOMATOPOEIA in the Glossary). In the 1970s a tight, skinny strapless top worn by British women was known as a 'boob-tube' (which is slang for a television in the USA).

breast

The origins of the word breast may lie in an ancient Indo-European (see Glossary) root word meaning 'bud' or 'to swell'. The medical term for breast is mammary gland – mammary comes from the Latin *mamma* meaning breast or NIPPLE.

On the outside, breasts consist of a nipple surrounded by a circle of dark, crinkly skin called the AREOLA. Inside both the female and male breast there is a gland and some tiny tubes, or ducts, which reach out to the nipple. In a girl (and in a few perfectly normal boys) these ducts branch out at puberty under the influence of sex HORMONES produced in the OVARIES (female) or TESTES (male) and a certain amount of fatty tissue is deposited.

During PREGNANCY more hormones, this time from the WOMB, make the ducts increase in number and milk-forming tissue grows around their ends. When a baby sucks on the nipple, by a process which isn't understood, yet another hormone is released from the pituitary gland (just under the brain) which makes the breast produce milk. How much milk a mother produces has nothing to do with the size of her breasts – small flat breasts can feed twins just as easily as large ones.

Like any part of the body, breasts can get diseases. It's a good idea for girls and boys to learn how their breasts feel so they'll quickly discover if a lump develops. This may be CANCER or just a harmless cyst. It's a type of cancer that tends to be prevalent in women but men can get it too.

The best way to do a breast self-examination is to lie down and raise one arm above your head. With the flats of the finger tips of the other hand, massage the breast in a circular fashion from the outside moving in towards the nipple. You then repeat this with the other hand on the other breast. Your doctor or health clinic will be able to show you how to do this properly. If you find any unusual lump, or any bleeding or discharge from the nipple, go to your doctor straight away. They'll either reassure you that there's nothing wrong or be able to act quickly and cure you.

Most teenage girls worry about their breasts at some time or another. Some girls and women have one breast that's a bit bigger than the other – although this hardly ever shows. Some women get so obsessed about the size of their breasts that they go to cosmetic surgeons to have their breasts made smaller or larger. It's unlikely that any responsible surgeon would perform this operation, called mammoplasty, on a teenager whose breasts may still be developing.

Whatever their size, breasts, especially the nipples, are EROGENOUS ZONES for many girls and women (and some men too), meaning that they get good sexual feelings when touched or kissed on this part of the body. This may explain why, in Victorian times, it was not thought polite to mention the word. At the dinner table chicken or turkey breast was called 'white meat' in order to spare the blushes of the ladies present. In the twentieth century, the term 'white meat' was also used to refer to a white woman's breasts or her VAGINA. Black or dark meat is slang for a black woman seen as a SEX OBJECT.

There are many slang words for breasts – most refer to size: apples, bags, bazongas, bazooms (from bosom), bazoonjies, big brown eyes, boobies, BOOBS, breastworks, cans, chi-chi, coconuts, globes, headlights, hooters, jugs (also dairies and milkers all from the connection with breast milk), norks (this is Australian, apparently from *Norco*, the name of a brand of dairy products which shows a cow with full udders on the wrapper), knockers, lungs, mangoes, maracas, melons, muffins, pair, snorbs, tits and titties, Bristols (short for Bristol Cities, rhyming slang for titties), Tale of Two Cities (the title of the novel by Charles Dickens, also rhyming slang for titties).

brewer's droop

Since the late sixteenth century this expression has been used (mostly in the UK) to mean IMPOTENCE, or the inability to get an ERECTION, caused by drinking too much alcohol.

broad

In the USA in the 1920s, 'broad' was popular slang for a sexually PROMISCUOUS young woman. Language experts think it may have come from BAWD, meaning PROSTITUTE, or from the phrase 'broad in the beam' used by sailors for a large, flat-bottomed boat. In the past 'broad' has also meant wide and open, coarse, unrefined, vulgar, LOOSE, gross and INDECENT.

In the 1960s feminists tried to reclaim this word and used it for a woman who was 'liberal, tolerant, unconfined and not limited or narrow in scope'. But the problem with trying to give old words new meanings is that not everyone agrees with you. In the novel *The World is Full of Married Men* (1968) by Jackie Collins (see BODICE RIPPER) a male character tells us exactly what he thought of broads, 'I've been married three times – each time to a beautiful girl with about as much thinking power as a rabbit. It must be a sickness with me – I marry stupid, dumb, beautiful broads.'

brothel

A building where a number of PROSTITUTES live or go to work is called a brothel. The word seems to have started life as an Old English verb meaning to waste away. From this it developed the meaning 'go to ruin' and later 'a worthless or abandoned fellow, a scoundrel or a wretch'. It wasn't always so negative – popular fifteenth-century religious dramas from York in England (known as Mystery Plays) referred to Jesus as a *brethell*. By the sixteenth century this word was used only to refer to an abandoned woman or a common prostitute. Around this time an establishment for prostitutes was called by the Italian word *bordello*, which came from a French word meaning a cabin, hut or small farm. A confusion of the terms 'bordel-house' and 'brothel's (or brethell's) house' ended up as the shortened word brothel.

Euphemisms (see Glossary) for a brothel include call house, cat house, RED LIGHT house (traditionally, brothels had red lamps hanging outside them), shooting gallery (where a man 'shoots' or EJACULATES), BAWDY house, a house of ill-repute, and chicken ranch (which got its name from a famous brothel in Gilbert, Texas where the poor, local famers paid for their sex with chickens). In America MASSAGE PARLOUR is a euphemism for a brothel because in many of them the women also sell sexual services (the GAY equivalent are called BATHS).

buddy

Originally shortened from brother, a buddy first meant a good male friend of a man and later came to mean a good friend of either sex. To someone with AIDS, a buddy is someone who looks after and stays with them until the end – a cross between a friend and a carer.

buggery

In Standard English, bugger and buggery are the correct legal terms for a sodomite and SODOMY. Both buggery and sodomy mean ANAL INTERCOURSE. There are a variety of slang uses: it can be a way of expressing annoyance as when people say 'Oh bugger!'; it can be used of a small, young or pleasing person or thing as in the phrase 'she's (or he's) a cute little bugger'; or it can mean exhausted as in 'I felt completely buggered'. As a verb, 'to bugger' can mean either to have sex by penetrating the ANUS or to have anal sex with an animal (see BESTIALITY).

There's a mixture of racism, religious intolerance and HOMO-PHOBIA buried in the history of the word buggery. It started with the Latin word for a Bulgarian. In the fourteenth century bugger (or *bougre* as it was spelled) came to mean a heretic, someone who held an unorthodox religious belief. This applied to Bulgarians because they did not belong to the Roman Catholic Church – this was in the days before Protestantism – but were members of the Greek Ortho-dox Church (from the Bulgarian point of view, of course, Catholics were the ones who held unorthodox or corrupt religious beliefs).

The word was then used for all HOMOSEXUALS since it was, and still is, widely believed that all GAY men practise buggery.

bumboy

This is an offensive term, mostly used by HETEROSEXUALS who fear or hate HOMOSEXUALS (see HOMOPHOBIA), for a young GAY PROSTI-TUTE. 'Bum' is a reference to ANAL INTERCOURSE. The West Indian term 'batty-boy' means an EFFEMINATE gay man (batty being slang for 'bottom'). See also CATAMITE.

bush

This is slang for a woman's pubic hair and for the VAGINA. Bush is also slang for a beard – the connection being that a beard surrounds a man's lips and a woman's pubic hair surrounds her vaginal lips, or LABIA. Bush is sometimes used (by men) for a sexually attractive girl or woman.

butch

Slang for a tough (male) youth or man, a mannish woman, a masculine-looking LESBIAN, or an ultra-masculine GAY man. The word is also used to describe the active partner in a HOMOSEXUAL relationship (although gay sex doesn't mean that one partner is always active and the other always passive). When used of a lesbian it is usually a term of abuse, and suggests a stereotype of a rough, boot-wearing woman with a short, cropped hairstyle (see DYKE), who is the opposite of the soft, feminine, supposedly passive lesbian stereotype who is often referred to as FEM or femme.

Before it became a part of American homosexual slang in the twentieth century, butch was a northern British dialect word for the youngest male child in a family, and slang for a rough, tough (HETEROSEXUAL) young man. The word may have been shortened from the verb 'to butcher' in the sense of an extremely rough and clumsy haircut. According to a professor at the American Barber College, the 'Butch' is a more radical version of the crew cut.

C

call-girl

In the 1940s this term emerged for a PROSTITUTE who advertised her services, usually as a 'model', on cards in shop-windows. The male client (see JOHN) would then call her up on the telephone to find out when she was available. Today many call-girls leave their cards inside telephone booths.

camp

If someone is camp it means they behave in a way which is thought to be characteristic of a HOMOSEXUAL. In Latin, *campus* means 'open field'. No one is quite sure how it managed to get such a different meaning although there is a theory that its roots lie in a sixteenth-century theatrical term 'camping' which meant the wearing of women's costumes by young male actors (women weren't allowed on the stage until the seventeenth century). This term may have come from *campagne*, the French word for countryside because travelling entertainers passed through the countryside. This theory sounds a bit unlikely as medieval French actors also entertained in towns and cities.

In the early 1900s camp became what's known as 'London street slang' to describe someone who acted in an exaggerated or theatrical manner. By the 1920s it referred to homosexuals and was first used by actors without any sense of disapproval. But by the 1930s, camp had gained an objectionable or slightly disreputable sense. Around this time the word crossed the Atlantic where it came to mean EFFEMINATE or 'something so outrageously artificial, affected, inappropriate, or out-of-date as to be considered amusing'.

Among male GAYS, camp behaviour often involves a slightly higher pitched voice, a fussy way of walking, a special use of arms and hands (called 'limp-wristed'), wearing quite showy or FEMININE clothes and the use of words such as 'darling' and 'gorgeous'. Amongst LESBIANS it often means a rather MASCULINE way of dressing, talking, walking and behaving (see BUTCH). It may seem like an act to others but to gays and lesbians themselves it merely feels like an expression of who and what they are.

The whole idea of 'camping it up', although it paints a picture of a stereotype which is never completely true (people are always more complex than a stereotype), is only very mildly negative about homosexuality. This might be considered surprising in a culture which is highly intolerant of gays and lesbians (see HOMOPHOBIA). Perhaps the long history of connections with the theatre has given it positive and pleasurable associations. Camp can be wonderful and outrageous fun. The film stars Tony Curtis (in *Some Like It Hot*) and Mae West, plus quite a lot of the actors in *The Rocky Horror Show*, are all considered 'High Camp'.

cancer

When certain body cells start to multiply uncontrollably they form a tumour, or carcinoma. The word comes from the Latin word which literally means 'crab'. According to the ancient Greek physician Galen, this illness got its name because the tumour becomes surrounded by a number of swollen veins which look like the many legs of a crab.

Cancer can appear anywhere in the body but there are four main sex organs which are prone to cancer: the BREASTS (most often in women); the TESTICLES; the CERVIX; and the WOMB. Every girl should learn how to give herself a regular breast self-examination (see under BREASTS). Boys should learn how to check their testicles for any unusual lumps (see under TESTICLES). All women who are sexually active should go for a regular test (at least every three years) to make sure they don't have cervical cancer (see under CERVICOGRAPHY and CERVICAL SMEAR TEST). If it's discovered in the early stages, cancer can be cured in most cases. Not everyone realizes this and, sadly, don't go to their doctor at the stage when they could be cured.

Candida albicans See THRUSH.

cap

This is another name for a CONTRACEPTIVE called the DIAPHRAGM. It's also known as a 'Dutch cap' because of its resemblance to the women's head-dress of Holland's national costume. (For more information see DIAPHRAGM.)

carnal knowledge

This is a legal term meaning SEXUAL INTERCOURSE. Carnal literally means 'of the flesh', from the Latin word *caro* meaning flesh. It was originally a piece of meat passed round at sacrifices and warriors' feasts. (The carnation flower got its name because of its flesh-pink colour.)

casanova

Giacomo Girolamo (or Giovanni Jacopo) Casanova de Seingalt (1725–1798) was an Italian adventurer, diplomat, historian, mathematician, composer, playwright and word expert. He's best known for his twelve-volume *Memoirs* in which he boasted of his many love affairs as well as the rapes and seductions he committed. He was clearly both obsessed by women and neurotically afraid of emotional involvement. As a result Casanova's name came to be used for any man who is reckoned to be a great lover or who has lots of love affairs (see also DON JUAN).

casting couch

This Hollywood term refers to the early male film moguls who insisted on having sex with young female actresses (or actors if they were HOMOSEXUAL) on the couch in their office before they cast them in a screen role. The practice was so common that in 1924 a PORNOGRAPHIC film was made with the title *The Casting Couch* in which a young woman gets to sign her contract only after she's had sex with the producer. Marilyn Monroe commented on the fix that aspiring actresses of her generation were in:

'I've slept with producers for work. I'd be a liar if I said I didn't ... All the girls did it. It was like part of the job. They wanted to sample the merchandise. If you didn't go along, there were another twenty-five girls who would.'

It's not uncommon, even today (see ABUSE and HARASSMENT).

castration

This has its roots in a Sanskrit (see Glossary) word which meant 'he cuts to pieces'. The verb to castrate generally means to deprive a male of his TESTICLES (see EUNUCH) but it also means to deprive a female of her OVARIES. Castration is also used in a symbolic sense meaning to weaken, to deprive of strength or vigour, or to EMASCULATE. A book or film which is censored because it is thought to be too political or sexual, is said to have been emasculated or castrated. When an animal has its reproductive organs removed, it is called 'spaying' (female) or 'gelding' (male).

catamite

This means a boy or young man kept by an older man (see PEDERAST) who has ANAL INTERCOURSE with him. Catamite is the Latin translation of 'Ganymede', the name of a handsome young man who, according to ancient Greek legend, was carried away to Mount Olympus by an eagle owned by Zeus to become the cupbearer, and perhaps sexual partner, of the male gods. The eagle became a constellation. In medieval times 'ganymede' became another term for a male HOMOSEXUAL. Modern slang for a catamite is BUMBOY.

celibate (*sell*-ee-bate)

Someone who, either by free choice or by custom or tradition, chooses not to marry or not to have SEXUAL INTERCOURSE is said to be celibate. It comes from the Latin for 'unmarried' and may have its roots in a combination of an Old English word meaning 'to live' and a Sanskrit word (see Glossary) meaning 'alone'.

Celibacy has played an important part in Christian thinking since the first century AD when St Paul claimed that celibacy was superior to marriage. In medieval times strict theologians recommended celibacy between married couples on Thursdays, in memory of Jesus' arrest, Fridays, in memory of the crucifixion, Saturdays, in honour of the Virgin Mary, Sundays, in memory of the resurrection, and Mondays, to commemorate the dead. That left Tuesdays and Wednesdays – except when there was a ban on sex because of fast days and holy days, for forty days before Easter, Pentecost and Christmas and so on. This didn't leave many days for a married couple to have sex. (There was also a big debate about whether they were allowed to enjoy it.)

In the sixteenth century Martin Luther noted how few priests and nuns obeyed their vows of celibacy and declared that celibacy was not a desirable condition. Since then the Protestant clergy have been allowed to marry. Roman Catholic priests are still required to be celibate, as are nuns – whatever their religion or sect – because they're regarded as being 'married to Christ'. Muslim priests and Jewish rabbis have never been expected to observe celibacy.

centrefold See PLAYBOY.

cervical cap (*ser*-vik-kl)
This is a smaller, more solid version of the CAP or DIAPHRAGM, which is a method of CONTRACEPTION. Because the cervical cap can be more easily knocked out of place during SEXUAL INTERCOURSE, it's only recommended for girls or women who are allergic to rubber latex diaphragms.

cervical smear test (*ser*-vik-kl)
A cervical smear, also called a 'Papanicolaou smear' or 'pap smear' for short, is a simple screening test for unusual or unhealthy cells known as pre-cancerous cells of the CERVIX which may lead to cancer. A girl or woman will be given a PELVIC EXAMINATION and a sample of cells from the cervix is then sent to a laboratory to be tested for abnormalities.

If the result of the smear is positive it means that some abnormal cells have been found. This does not necessarily mean cancer. Mild cell abnormality (called dysplasia) often returns to normal without any treatment although the patient will probably be given a more thorough examination called a colposcopy. If the cell change is more serious, treatment may involve an out-patient procedure involving a laser or freezing of the cervix via the colposcope (an operating microscope).

Doctors recommend a smear test within the first year of sexual activity and every three years subsequently. A girl or woman should definitely have the test done once a year if she is on the PILL, has had a genital HERPES virus, a genital WART (also a virus), or a SEXUALLY TRANSMITTED DISEASE called CHLAMYDIA. She also falls into a high risk category if she smokes and/or has had many sexual partners or started having sexual intercourse at a young age. Probably because SPERMICIDES kill viruses as well as sperm, it's thought that those who use a DIAPHRAGM or CONDOM are less likely to develop abnormal cervix cells than those who use another contraceptive or use no BIRTH CONTROL at all. Having a regular smear test is one way in which a woman can take control of her own health and prevent cancer. If discovered in its early stages cervical cancer can be treated successfully.

cervicography (ser-vee-*kog*-raff-ee)
Like a CERVICAL SMEAR TEST, this will check for abnormal cells of the CERVIX. During a PELVIC EXAMINATION, a specially designed 'endocervical brush' is used to take a photograph of the cervix which is sent to a gynaecologist for assessment.

cervix (*ser*-vix)
The biological name for the cervix is the Latin term *cervix uteri*, which means 'neck of the UTERUS'. The cervix is at the very top of the VAGINA and feels a bit like a nose with a small dimple in the middle. It is a powerful ring of muscle with a very narrow passage running through the middle. These muscles relax during childbirth to allow the baby to pass through.

The cervix is one part of the female sex organs which is prone to

CANCER. Like many cancers today, if it's discovered early it can be cured (see CERVICAL SMEAR TEST, CERVICOGRAPHY).

chancre (shanker)

From the same Latin word from which we get CANCER, a chancre is the earliest sign of the SEXUALLY TRANSMITTED DISEASE called SYPHILIS. A chancre is a small painless lump that usually appears on the LABIA or vaginal lips, on the PENIS, or sometimes by the mouth or ANUS. Unless it develops into an ulcer, a chancre may go unnoticed. It disappears after a short while as the disease spreads to the rest of the body. This does not mean the disease has gone away. Anyone who notices an ulcer – or anything unusual – on their GENITALS must go to their doctor or to a SPECIAL CLINIC which specializes in sexually transmitted diseases.

chancroid (*shan*-kroyd)

This is a rare SEXUALLY TRANSMITTED DISEASE, sometimes also called SOFT SORE. It gets its name from the Latin word meaning 'to resemble' presumably because the sufferer gets an ulcer which looks very much like a CHANCRE, the first symptom of SYPHILIS. However, unlike a chancre, a chancroid ulcer is painful and doesn't go away. Anyone who notices a sore, ulcer, or anything unusual on their GENITALS should go to their doctor or to a SPECIAL CLINIC that specializes in VENEREAL DISEASES.

change of life See MENOPAUSE.

chaste/chastity (chayst/chass-tit-tee)

From the Latin word for holy or morally pure, chaste can mean not having sex with anyone outside marriage, not having SEXUAL INTERCOURSE at all (see CELIBATE), pure in thought and act or austere or simple in design. Lurking behind these meanings is the Christian idea dating back to the biblical writings of St Paul that sex defiles, which literally means 'makes dirty'. This was thought to be especially true of women who were seen to be unable to control their sexual appetites because they supposedly lacked the mental powers of reasoning that men had.

A chastity belt was a device usually made of leather on a metal framework which was locked round a woman's GENITALS to prevent her from having SEXUAL INTERCOURSE with anyone who didn't own both the key and her – usually the husband. They were probably invented in the East in the thirteenth century. They may have been designed to protect a woman from being raped, but jealous husbands who were convinced that women were unable to control their sexual appetites also made their wives wear them. Today the sight of a chastity belt in a museum usually raises a laugh – but it doesn't take much imagination to work out how painful and unhygienic they must have been to the women who were forced to wear them. Some historians doubt that they were ever actually used.

cheesecake

During the Second World War (1939–1945), American GIs invented (see NEOLOGISM in the Glossary) this term for photos of scantily-dressed glamorous women – another word for a PIN-UP. It soon became used for any sexually attractive young woman. It probably came from the fact that 'cheesey' rhymes with 'easy' (a reference to sexual PROMISCUITY) and Black American slang use of 'cake' meaning VAGINA. Another theory is that the Jewish restaurants in New York's entertainment district on 42nd Street and around Times Square used to have window-displays of desserts next door to theatres which displayed publicity photos of nearly naked chorus girls. Apparently, when asked what they were looking at, hen-pecked husbands would reply 'cheesecake'. See BEEFCAKE.

cherry

In the sixteenth century cherry was a term of endearment for a woman, probably from the French term *cherie* which means 'beloved' and from which we also get the word cherish. Three hundred and fifty years later, 'cherry pie' was an affectionate term for an attractive woman. In the 1950s, perhaps influenced by the male chauvinist idea that an attractive woman is like a sweet, ripe fruit, ready for picking and eating (by a man), the word cherry was slang for the HYMEN and for female VIRGINITY (see also MAIDENHEAD). Cherry is also used by

GAYS to mean a male who has not yet been anally penetrated (see ANAL SEX). In America a cherry-picker is slang for a man who sexually desires young girls (see LOLITA) and, among gays, for a long, thin PENIS.

child sexual abuse

The sexual ABUSE of children is the criminal exploitation of a physically and emotionally immature person through INCEST, MOLESTATION or RAPE. Most sexual abusers of children are men (see PAEDOPHILIA) and the majority of children they abuse are girls, but boys are also sexually abused and some abusers are older children. Most incidents take place with someone the child knows – a father, step-father or other close relative, or a man who lives nearby and is probably trusted by the family.

Many abusers try to keep children silent by telling them that it is their 'special secret'. But it is very important for the child to tell someone. Children who bottle it all up often end up very confused and disturbed about all sexual relationships, even non-exploitational and loving ones. It's not always easy to tell someone about being sexually abused – especially if it is one of your parents who is abusing you. A teacher or doctor you trust will probably be understanding. There are also counselling services and helplines you can call (see COUNSELLING).

The abuser will often try to make the child feel that she or he is in some way responsible for what is happening to them. This makes the child feel guilty and too scared to tell anyone what has been done to them. But a child is *never* a guilty party in any case of sexual abuse. It is always the adult who is guilty.

chlamydia (klam-*id*-ee-ah)

Caused by a microscopic parasite, chlamydia is the most common SEXUALLY TRANSMITTED DISEASE. Symptoms in women can include constant and painful peeing (see CYSTITIS), a thin discharge from the VAGINA, and sometimes a painful feeling in the lower abdomen which might be accompanied by fever. Men usually get a burning feeling when they pee and may experience a discharge from the PENIS. Some people get no symptoms at all. In this way it's very much like another sexually transmitted disease called GONORRHOEA, with which it's often confused. Many people with chlamydia often have gonorrhoea as well, but curing one of these diseases does not mean the other one will go away. They each need a different type of antibiotic.

If you or your partner had any of the symptoms described above you should both go to your doctor or a SPECIAL CLINIC that deals with sexually transmitted diseases. You should use a CONDOM when having sex, until the illness is completely cured.

chromosome (*kroam*-o-soam)
From the Greek *khroma* meaning 'colour' and *soma* meaning 'body', a chromosome is one of a number of rod-shaped parts in the nucleus, or centre, of a cell which contains genes that determine the characteristics of every living thing. We inherit our chromosomes from the OVUM and SPERM of our parents. The sex chromosomes control all the genetic information involving sex. They determine the shape and size of our body, BREASTS, and sex organs, and they control HORMONE production. The human female has one pair of X chromosomes; the human male has one X and one Y chromosome.

circumcision
The first part of this word means 'round' from the same Latin word from which we also get 'circus', 'circumference' etc. The last part is from the Latin 'to cut', from which we also get 'scissors'. Circumcision is the cutting away of the FORESKIN of the PENIS. (For female circumcision, see CLITORIDECTOMY.)

Circumcision was originally a religious PUBERTY rite in ancient Egypt where it was performed on boys around the age of thirteen, as they entered manhood. When the Hebrews brought back the idea from Egypt, they pushed the age back to the eighth day after birth, made it compulsory, and turned what had been a pagan rite into an article of the Jewish faith.

Islam adopted the custom of circumcision (changing the age to eight years) and it also became commonplace among the Maya, the Aztecs, the Incas, and Aboriginals in Australia and in some parts of Polynesia. In the twentieth century European and North American doctors decided baby boys should be circumcised for health reasons. Under the foreskin of an uncircumcised penis there are glands which produce a secretion called SMEGMA. If the foreskin is too tight to be drawn back or isn't washed properly, smegma can collect as a white cheesey-smelling substance which may be involved in causing CANCER either of the penis or of the CERVIX of an uncircumcised man's regular partner.

But many doctors today point out that a tight foreskin is perfectly normal in a young infant and will ease up as he gets older. Regular washing is all that's needed to keep the penis free from smegma. An operation on a boy's penis, whatever his age, can cause unnecessary mental anguish.

In the UK a circumcised penis is sometimes called a roundhead and an uncircumcised one a cavalier. This refers back to the English Civil War (1642–1645) when Oliver Cromwell's soldiers, called Roundheads, wore smooth plain helmets and King Charles II's Cavaliers wore flashy hats with frills and feathers. Other slang terms include clipped or low neck and short sleeves (circumcised), and blind or near-sighted (uncircumcised).

clap

This used to be Standard English for the SEXUALLY TRANSMITTED DISEASE now called GONORRHOEA until about 1840, when it became a low colloquialism. (See Glossary for these language terms.) The word originates from the medieval French word *clapoir* which meant a swelling in the groin – one of the later symptoms in some men.

climacteric

From the Greek word meaning 'a rung of a ladder' (see also CLIMAX), when climacteric first entered the English language in the sixteenth century it meant 'a major turning point' or 'a critical stage'. It now means both the female MENOPAUSE and the time in the life of a man when his sexual powers are reduced. This is usually when he's in his sixties.

climax

Climax, another word for an ORGASM, comes from the Greek word for ladder. Climax also means the highest point or culmination, the final stage in a process, and an event or point of the greatest intensity or interest.

clitoridectomy (klit-or-ee-*dekt*-om-ee)

From the Greek word for 'outside', the suffix (see Glossary) '–ectomy' means 'the surgical removal of'. Clitoridectomy is a form of female GENITAL mutilation sometimes known as female CIRCUMCISION, involving cutting out all or part of the CLITORIS. It's practised in several Arab and African societies by Muslims, Christians and some other religions.

In its least severe form, called *Sunna*, just the GLANS is removed. In 'full excision', part or all of the clitoris (which is buried quite deep inside the body) and part of the inner LABIA are removed. In its most extreme form, called 'Pharaonic circumcision', the clitoris and labia are completely removed and the two sides of the VULVA are stitched together, leaving only a small opening for the flow of MENSTRUAL blood and URINE. This sewing together is known as 'infibulation' from the Latin word for 'pierce, clasp'. Traditionally, if an infibulated woman is not reopened before her wedding night by a midwife who uses a knife or other sharp instrument, she is forced to submit to sexual intercourse by her new husband which is extremely painful (and sometimes impossible) for both partners.

The pain suffered by young women as they are clitoridectomized is immense. The health and medical consequences can be horrendous. Amongst those communities who practise it, however, it is regarded as an essential part of a girl's growing up. Many women know that an uncircumcised girl will never find a husband. Many men feel they need proof of their bride's VIRGINITY.

Opposition to female circumcision is growing among Arabs and Africans. Many countries now have laws prohibiting it.

clitoris

Language experts who delve into the origins of words, called etymologists (see Glossary), are confused about where the word clitoris comes from. One suggestion is the Greek word meaning 'to shut'.

Another is the Greek for 'little hill'. In ancient mythology the clitoris was personified as a queen of the Amazons called Kleite and yet another theory (an unlikely one) claims that *kleitoris* meant 'divine, famous, goddess-like'.

The clitoris is an important part of the female's external sex organs. It's placed at the top of the VULVA where the inner lips, or LABIA, meet which form a hood of skin known as the PREPUCE. It has a tip called the GLANS and a shaft which mostly lies underneath the skin. During sexual FOREPLAY and MASTURBATION, when the glans is touched, stroked, or kissed (see CUNNILINGUS) blood flows into the clitoris and it becomes ERECT. If the rubbing and stroking continues, sexual excitement will increase to the point of ORGASM. Just before she COMES, the clitoris usually does a dive back down but the glans remains poking out. After she's had an orgasm it may feel very tender but some women enjoy further stimulation in order to come once or several times more (see MULTIPLE ORGASM).

It used to be thought that a clitoral orgasm was what VIRGINS experienced when they masturbated and that a more mature orgasm, called a vaginal orgasm, could only be achieved through SEXUAL INTERCOURSE. But most girls and women report that all their orgasms are a bit different and that as long as the clitoris is being stimulated it doesn't matter whether they are masturbating or having sexual intercourse. Some sexual positions during sexual intercourse, such as the MISSIONARY POSITION for example, make it quite difficult for the clitoris to be stimulated. Others, such as when she is sitting on top of him, mean that either she or he can use a hand to stimulate the clitoris.

closet

From the French word meaning 'little enclosure', closet entered the English language in the fourteenth century for an apartment or a small, private room. From this word developed the sense of 'a state or condition of secrecy, privacy or obscurity' and closet came to be used to describe someone who hid her or his actions or real thoughts. Meanwhile the word also came to mean a cabinet for storing utensils, clothing or china. Today the word closet is mostly used in North America. The British tend to call it a cupboard (from the wooden boards on which cups were stored).

Eventually, the expression 'closet QUEEN' came to be used to describe a man who is actually HOMOSEXUAL but who pretends to the rest of the world that he is HETEROSEXUAL. In the 1960s this changed to 'closet GAY' to include LESBIANS. 'To come out of the closet', sometimes shortened to 'COME OUT', means to make one's homosexuality public knowledge.

cock

Cock entered the English language in the fifteenth century to mean 'a spout or tap'. In 1599 Shakespeare used the word in *Henry V* (Part 2) to refer to an erect PENIS: 'And Pistol's cock is up'. Around this time the verb 'to cock' came to mean 'to stand or stick upright'. In his play *Amends for Ladies* (1610), the British actor and dramatist Nathan Field wrote, 'O man, what art thou when thy cock is up?', suggesting that when a man has an ERECTION he doesn't listen to his conscience.

The penis does have some similarities with a tap: both have an internal valve which regulates the flow of liquid. The valve in a penis ensures that males can't URINATE and EJACULATE at the same time. Cock meaning PENIS was Standard English until the 1940s when it became a vulgarism (see Glossary).

From this use of cock came two further meanings, 'a swaggering boastful male' and 'the leader of a group or organisation'. But the behaviour of a cockerel surrounded by a group of hens makes it likely that these meanings were also influenced by the arrogant and aggressive sexual behaviour of the male bird – from which we get the expression 'cock of the walk'.

Cock used in the sense of nonsense-talk, as in the phrase, 'that's a load of old cock', doesn't have anything to do with penises or cockerels but is short for 'poppycock' which comes from the Dutch word *pappekak*, literally meaning soft dung. It is also a shortened form of 'cock-and-bull story' which first meant 'a long rambling tale' and later came to mean what it does today – 'an incredible story told as if it were true'.

cock or **crotch cheese** See SMEGMA.

cock sucker
This is a TABOO and derogatory term (see Glossary) for a partner who plays the female role in a male HOMOSEXUAL relationship (see FELLATIO), for someone who tries to curry favour with a superior (also called an arse or ass kisser or licker), and it's a degrading name applied to any person (usually a male) who isn't liked, especially a sneak.

cocktease
Also known as pricktease, this is an insulting term for a girl or woman who sexually arouses a boy or man but then refuses to go any further. There's a DOUBLE STANDARD here because females are supposed to make themselves sexually attractive for men and at the same time keep themselves 'pure' (see CHASTE).

coil
This is a widely-used term for a CONTRACEPTIVE method called the IUD which stands for INTRAUTERINE DEVICE. 'Intrauterine' means inside the UTERUS, or WOMB. They come in various shapes, some of which look like a coil. (See also BIRTH CONTROL.)

coitus (ko-*ee*-tus)
Based on the Latin word meaning 'to come together', this is the formal word for SEXUAL INTERCOURSE between female and male. Coition means exactly the same thing.

coitus interruptus
This is the formal term for SEXUAL INTERCOURSE in which the PENIS is withdrawn before EJACULATION. It is not, however, a reliable form of CONTRACEPTION.

come
'To come' means to have an ORGASM. As a noun 'come', sometimes spelled 'cum' in North America, is slang for SEMEN. The expression

'come on' can mean that a girl has started her PERIOD. It's also used in the expression 'to give the come on' meaning to flirt or show strong sexual interest. A 'real come on' is someone or something that makes you feel very sexually aroused.

come out See CLOSET.

conceive

This word comes from a Latin word which means both 'be pregnant' and 'understand mentally' – babies and ideas are both conceived.

Conception takes place when a SPERM penetrates and unites with an EGG CELL (or OVUM) resulting in the start of a new life. This is also called FERTILIZATION.

conception

From the Latin word meaning 'be pregnant', conception is said to take place when a male seed, or SPERM, fertilizes a female egg cell, or OVUM.

During SEXUAL INTERCOURSE when the male has an ORGASM, he EJACULATES probably as many as 300 million sperm into the VAGINA. The sperm then flow into the WOMB and from there into the FALLOPIAN TUBES. If this happens just after an egg cell has been released from one of the woman's OVARIES (a process called OVULA-TION), a single sperm may enter the egg cell. At this point she has conceived, the egg is FERTILIZED, and she is PREGNANT.

concubine

From the Latin meaning 'to lie with', a concubine is a woman who lives or cohabits with a man without being married to him. The word has a notion of higher status than PROSTITUTE or a 'kept woman', which can perhaps be explained by its history. In Roman times concubinage was recognized by the State and a concubine's children were not considered illegitimate. In British society the word was used for an officially-recognized MISTRESS of royalty or even, in medieval times, a priest.

Dictionaries often define a concubine simply as 'a mistress'. But this doesn't give the true picture since, unlike a mistress who is a 'kept woman' and owned by the man who pays for her, a concubine's position was socially equal and publicly acceptable. This idea of equality may have something to do with the fact that in the fifteenth century a male lover could be called a concubine. And in America today, although it's only rarely used, a man who cohabits with either a woman or another man may be called a concubine.

condom

This is a sheath worn on the PENIS during SEXUAL INTERCOURSE to prevent PREGNANCY and the spread of SEXUALLY TRANSMITTED DISEASES. There are several theories about the origins of the condom. The word first appeared in a poem called *A Scots Answer to a British Vision* by John Hamilton, second Baron of Belhaven in 1706. Other theories include a Dr Quondam, the French town named Condom, the Persian word *kondu* meaning animal intestines used to store grain, and the Latin word *condere* meaning 'to contain'. In truth, no one really knows.

Condoms have been used for centuries. The earliest example is a cave-painting at Les Combarelles in central France dated between 15,000 BC and 10,000 BC which shows a man wearing one. In ancient Egypt sheaths may have been worn as a sign of high rank and to keep off flies.

In 1564 the Italian physician Gabriel Fallopo (see FALLOPIAN TUBE) recommended the use of linen sheaths soaked in herbal brews to protect a man from getting SYPHILIS. These clearly didn't work so they began to be made of intestines of sheep, calves, goats, and possibly fish bladders. The earliest reference to a condom being used to prevent pregnancy seems to be an early work of PORNOGRAPHY called *L'Escolle des Filles* (The Girls' School) by Michel Millot published in English in 1666.

Shakespeare referred to what we now call a condom as a 'Venus glove'. They were not popular with the seventeenth-century French writer Madame de Sevigné, who described them as 'armour against enjoyment and a spider web against danger'; but were much appreciated by the Italian adventurer CASANOVA who called them *redingotes d'Angleterre*, meaning 'English overcoats', and wrote of them as 'that wonderful preventive against an accident which might lead to frightful repentence'. They were not appreciated by the fervently religious Englishman Joseph Cam who wrote in 1734 that 'to publish methods of prevention smells so rank of the Libertine and Freethinker that it ought not to be allowed in a Christian country'. They are still not acceptable to Roman Catholic doctrine which rejects all forms of birth control other than the WITHDRAWAL method.

A bit more social history about the condom is provided by the entry for 'cundum' in a book called *Dictionary of the Vulgar Tongue, Buckish Slang, University Wit and Pickpocket Eloquence* (1785):

'The dried gut of a sheep, worn by men in the act of coition, to prevent venereal infection; said to be invented by one Colonel Cundum. These machines were long prepared and sold by a matron of the name of Philips, at the Green Canister, in Half-Moon-Street, in the Strand. That good lady having acquired a fortune, retired from business; but learning that the town was not well served by her successors, she, out of a patriotic zeal for the public welfare, returned to her occupation; of which she gave notice by divers hand-bills, in circulation in the year 1776.'

In the nineteenth century condoms were cumbersome things to make as well as to wear as this printed instruction reveals:

'Take the caecum (large intestine) of the sheep; soak it first in water, turn it on both sides, then repeat the operation in a weak ley (solution) of soda, which must be changed every four or five hours, for five or six successive times; then move the mucous membrane with the nail; sulphur, wash in clean water, and then in soap and water; rinse, inflate and dry. Next cut it to the required length, and attach a piece of ribbon to the open end. Use to prevent infection or pregnancy.'

The invention of vulcanized rubber in 1843 meant condoms could be mass-produced and more comfortable to use. Late nineteenth-century manufacturers in England tried to give their product an air of dignity by using packaging which had colour portraits of Prime Minister William Gladstone, and Queen Victoria who, with nine children, did not set a good example. Condoms are now made of thin latex and are widely used today both to prevent pregnancy and as an important part of SAFER SEX, since they're the only contraceptive which can also prevent the spread of HIV. For male HOMOSEXUALS who practise ANAL SEX there are also thicker condoms available for this purpose. Condoms now come in a variety of colours and flavours – some even glow in the dark.

A condom has to be put on (both partners can share in this) when the penis is erect. The more reliable ones have a little teat at the top which has to be squeezed while it's being unrolled down to the base of the penis so that no air gets trapped inside which might make it burst. When the male EJACULATES, the SEMEN stays inside the condom. This prevents sperm from getting into the VAGINA which can cause pregnancy. Because the body fluids of both partners don't come into contact, there is a reduced risk of any sexually transmitted disease. When the penis is withdrawn it's important to hold the condom in place or semen may leak out as the erection goes down.

Condoms aren't one hundred per cent safe – out of every hundred couples using the condom for a year, about four women fall pregnant. Because they can burst or slip off, it's a good idea for the girl or woman to use a SPERMICIDE – especially one which contains the chemical NONOXYNOL 9, since this kills both the sperm and the HIV virus.

Slang terms for a condom include rubber, sheath, safe, lifesaver (Australian), johnny, noddy (possible from the shape of the hat with a little bell worn by the character in Enid Blyton's children's books), diving bell, preventive, preservative, protective, prophylactic, pro, bag, joy-bag, CUM bag, scum-bag, splatter-bag, balloon, envelope, French letter, (the French refer to a *capote anglaise* meaning English cloak or hood), raincoat, jacket, boot, glove, hat shower cap, skin, fishskin, Manhattan eel, Coney Island whitefish, dunky, flunky, plonker (which is also UK slang for a penis), thingy, coso ('thing' in Italian), Durex, Mates (UK brand names), Trojan (US brand name).

One last bit of social history: the public was amused to learn that the British Army ordered special camouflage-coloured condoms during the 1991 Gulf War for protecting rifles from sand. Condoms and war have a long history: the eighteenth-century *Dictionary of the Vulgar Tongue* mentioned that a condom was 'also a false scabbard over a sword, and the oil-skin case for holding the colours (flags) of a regiment'.

See also FEMALE CONDOM.

contact tracing See SPECIAL CLINIC.

contraception

'Contra' means against and 'ception' is short for CONCEPTION. Any device or method, whether artificial or natural, which prevents a SPERM from fertilizing an EGG CELL is called a contraceptive or a BIRTH CONTROL method.

For methods of contraception, see the PILL, MINI-PILL, IUD, MORNING-- AFTER PILL, SPERMICIDE, RHYTHM METHOD, COITUS INTERRUPTUS, CONDOM, FEMALE CONDOM, and DIAPHRAGM.

coprophilia (kop-ro-*fil*-ee-a)

The Greek word for 'dung' is *kopros*. From this we get several English words related to FAECES. Coprophilia is a sexual PERVERSION involving a fascination with faeces or filth. Coprography is the impulse to write or draw OBSCENE material, especially words connected with shit or sexual activities involving the anus. Coprolalia is the irresistible impulse to say 'dirty' words, particularly slang words for faeces — it's often a sign of a mental disturbance such as schizophrenia. Coprophagia, the eating of faeces, is a symptom sometimes found in people with very severe schizophrenia.

copulation

From the Latin word meaning 'to bond' or 'to fasten or tie together' (from which we also get the word 'couple'), this is a formal term for SEXUAL INTERCOURSE. A synonym (see Glossary) is COITUS.

corpus luteum

In Latin *luteus* means 'golden yellow' and *corpus* means 'body'. It is the medical term for a small, yellowish structure of cells which forms on the OVARY where an EGG CELL is released during OVULA- TION. The corpus luteum produces several hormones, including

PROGESTERONE which makes the lining of the WOMB grow in preparation for pregnancy. If the egg cell is not FERTILIZED, the yellow body withers away and is shed through the vagina when a girl or woman has her PERIOD.

cottaging

In British slang, GAY men who hang around outside of public toilets waiting for sexual encounters are said to go 'cottaging'. In the USA they go 'tea-housing'. The terms are a form of word-play, reflecting the fact that in reality gay men aren't able to meet each other openly in warm comfortable places (see HOMOPHOBIA).

counselling

When you have some sort of sexual problem, talking to someone who is professionally trained can really help. Friends, family, and teachers can provide a good shoulder to cry on but they may not know exactly what to do next. There are organisations dedicated to providing young people with counselling, help and advice for almost every problem under the sun, but finding them isn't always easy. The following tips should help put you in touch with a wide variety of counselling services and professional problem-solvers. You can check out the sex education books in the library or in a bookshop – many have a list of useful addresses and phone numbers, look in the phone directory or Yellow Pages under the subject you want, phone your doctor or local hospital, phone or visit the Citizen's Advice Bureau, contact the British Association for Counselling (0788-578328), or The Children's Legal Centre (071-359 6251). Your local Samaritans helpline (under Samaritans in the phone book) will also help the despairing or suicidal on a wide variety of subjects.

On specific problems the following organisations will help you find your nearest clinic or advice centre: for HIV/AIDS contact the Terrence Higgins Trust Helpline (071-242 1010); for sexual abuse phone Childline (Freephone 0800 1111); for contraception/pregnancy/abortion look in the phone book under 'Family Planning' or 'Pregnancy' or contact the Family Planning Association (071-636 7866); for lesbian and gay advice contact the Lesbian and Gay Youth

Movement (081-317 9690) or the Lesbian and Gay Switchboard (071-837 7324); for sexually transmitted diseases look up in the phone book under any of the following: Special Clinic, Venereal Disease, Venereology, Sexually Transmitted Disease, STD, Urogenital, or call your local hospital or doctor.

Many of these organisations operate helplines, some of which operate 24 hours a day, 365 days a year. Their lines are often engaged, so keep trying. They will all be sympathetic and you can remain anonymous if you want. Don't ever think you have to face a problem on your own.

cow

These gentle, harmless animals who have provided the human race with food, drink and clothing for thousands of years have also provided English-speakers with several words and expressions connected to sex – mostly with unpleasant connotations (see Glossary). In the 1690s a cow was a lazy SLUT of a woman; by the nineteenth century it was slang for a HARLOT.

Many words related to cows have become sexual slang words. Slang terms for female BREASTS include 'dairies' and 'jugs'. CREAM is slang for SEMEN and 'to cream one's jeans' means to get very excited about something. CHEESECAKE and BEEFCAKE are slang for a woman or man who is seen as a SEX OBJECT.

crabs

The tiny lice which infest the PUBIC region (and often spread to the rest of the body hair) are commonly called crabs because they look a bit like crabs. Their Latin name is *phthirus pubis*.

Pubic lice can be spread by SEXUAL INTERCOURSE or by coming into contact with clothes or bedding which is infected with the lice or their eggs, called nits. They feed by sucking human blood and cause an itchiness which drives people crazy. Although you often find them in unhygienic conditions, crabs aren't that fussy about whether you're clean or dirty. The only way to get rid of them is by using a special lotion from the chemist. You also have to boil, bleach and tumble dry all clothing that might be infested.

crack

Since the sixteenth century this has been slang for a VAGINA. In the eighteenth century it meant a female PROSTITUTE. In the nineteenth century the term 'crack hunter', with associations of chasing and painfully killing a wild animal, referred to a PENIS.

Crack is also the name of a cocaine-based drug. There probably isn't a connection with any of the slang uses of crack mentioned above, although the worlds of drugs, sex and crime often share the same pool of words.

cream

The American poet Walt Whitman (1819–1891) defined cream as 'Father-stuff' meaning SEMEN. The expression 'to cream one's jeans' means to be in a state of excitement (not necessarily sexual) about something.

cross-dressing

Also known as wearing drag, this means wearing the clothes of the opposite GENDER, although it usually refers to a male who wears female clothes. As it's socially acceptable for a woman to wear trousers it's more difficult to tell if a woman is cross-dressing. Someone who gets a sexual kick from cross-dressing is called a TRANSVESTITE.

cruising

In the 1950s this American slang expression referred to young men who cruised the streets in their cars looking for young women to pick up. By the late 1960s it was mainly used by GAY men walking the streets looking for sexual encounters.

crush

When they've reached PUBERTY, it's very common for girls and boys to develop a sudden and intense feeling of infatuation or sexual attraction towards someone – perhaps an older girl or boy, a pop star, a footballer, a friend, or even a teacher. It used to be called a 'pash', short for passion.

The feeling usually passes, but at the time it feels very real. If you get a crush on someone of the same sex you may wonder if you're GAY. But many people who turn out to be HETEROSEXUAL will admit, if they're honest, that they once had a crush on someone of the same sex – and lots of gays and LESBIANS had crushes on someone of the opposite sex. Our sexual preferences aren't decided by the sort of FANTASIES we have, and our sexual fantasies don't necessarily indicate what our sexual preferences are.

cuckold

This word is largely obsolete (see Glossary) these days, but it's been used since the thirteenth century to mean a husband who has an unfaithful wife. The word comes from the activities of the female cuckoo, who lays her eggs in the nest of another bird. According to the myth, a cuckolded man grows horns and is weak and very silly – presumably because he can't control his wife like a 'real' man should.

The cuckold has always been laughed at – Shakespeare rocked his audiences with endless jokes, puns and *double entendres* (see Glossary) about them. In some Mediterranean countries when people want to suggest a man's wife is being unfaithful with other men, they still make the sign of horns, either by putting two fingers to their forehead or by raising a hand with the little and first fingers sticking up.

Around the beginning of the seventeenth century the word cuckquean (see QUEEN) was used for a woman whose husband was unfaithful, but this word has become obsolete.

cunnilingus

The meaning of this Latin term is easy to work out once you know that 'cunni' comes from *cunnus* meaning VULVA and 'lingus' is from *lingere* meaning to lick. The formal definition is 'oral stimulation of the female GENITALS'. Cunnilingus involves the licking, sucking and KISSING of the CLITORIS, vulva and entrance to the VAGINA by tongue movements. For many couples it's a normal and loving part of FOREPLAY or of giving a woman an ORGASM.

Because fluids from both the mouth and the VAGINA can contain HIV, cunnilingus is not part of SAFER SEX. However, because there is no evidence that HIV survives in the mouth or stomach, it is much safer than unprotected SEXUAL INTERCOURSE. Another infection which can be passed between the mouth and the genitals is HERPES. Those who enjoy cunnilingus and want to minimize the risk of infection should use a DENTAL DAM.

Slang terms for cunnilingus include going down, giving head, box lunch, dipping in the BUSH, dining at the Y (a reference to the shape of a woman with her legs spread out rather than to the YMCA), muff diving, hair pie, eating pussy, and BLOW JOB (in the USA only – in the UK this means FELLATIO).

cunt

Originally Standard English (see Glossary) for the female PUDENDUM, this is often referred to as the 'c-word' (see FOUR-LETTER WORD).

The first-known reference is in *Gropecuntlane*, the name of a street in Oxford in early medieval times. There was a street with the same name in London in the thirteenth century which may have been a RED-LIGHT district, the haunt of PROSTITUTES.

There are several theories about the origins of 'cunt'. It may be related to the Latin *cuneus* meaning wedge, or to the Old Norse *kunte* meaning female pudenda, from an older word meaning prostitute which, in turn, may have come from a prehistoric Germanic word meaning 'female GENITALS'. Another theory suggests that its roots lie in a northern Greek dialect word, *quda*, meaning round or curved. Yet another theory claims it comes from the Old English word *queynte*, now 'quaint', which originally meant wise, crafty or cunning but now means pleasantly odd or old-fashioned. Another Old English word, *cwithe* meaning 'womb', may be the source, or a basic Old English root which indicated something that was essentially feminine.

By the fifteenth century it dropped out of formal or polite English and became what is known as a vulgarism (see Glossary). In Shakespeare's *Twelfth Night*, the lovesick Malvolio gets as close as he can to using the word when, reading a letter he thinks to be from his lady-love, he exclaims:

'By my life, this is my lady's hand: These are her very C's, her U's 'n' her T's; and thus she makes her great P's.'

(See SCATOLOGY.)

By 1700 'cunt' was declared legally OBSCENE and no publisher dared print it in full until the 1960s. Dictionaries went to absurd lengths to get round the problem – sometimes using the Greek for VULVA, or leaving dashes, as in 'C---'. Showing just how much disgust both the word and the female genitals caused, one late eighteenth-century English dictionary of slang defined it as, 'C**T ... a nasty word for a nasty thing.'

The history of this word tells us a lot about attitudes towards women and their sexuality. Even though it can now be printed, very few newspapers dare to use the word. A film can get away with showing scenes of torture, murder and RAPE, but the censors reach for their scissors once an actor says 'cunt'. As a term of abuse, cunt is widely thought to be much worse than either 'prick', which tends to mean foolish rather than disgusting, or even 'shit' which often means 'worthless'.

curse

Originally, a curse was a prayer to the gods asking them to inflict some sort of harm or injury upon an enemy. In the nineteenth century the expression 'the curse of Eve' was used informally for a woman's PERIOD. Later shortened to 'the curse', this term reflects the idea that God cursed women for the sin that Eve committed in the Garden of Eden. Although Adam sinned too, traditionally Eve has always been blamed.

Historically, a menstruating woman has often been cursed by people around her. Today strict Orthodox Jews still obey an Old Testament ruling:

'When a woman has a discharge of blood which is her regular discharge from her body, she shall be in her impurity for seven days and whoever touches her shall be unclean until the evening ... And if any man lies with her at all ... he shall be unclean seven days ...' (Leviticus)

Other people and religions have shown the same sort of disgust towards a menstruating female. At various times in history she has been accused of making cows ABORT their calves, of turning milk sour, of making bread fail to rise, and even of making razors go blunt. It's possible that these ideas come from the fact that a woman is unlikely to become pregnant when she has her period.

Many people still think that a woman whose 'curse is upon her' shouldn't make love. But there is no reason why she shouldn't, unless she doesn't feel like it. Many women say that they actually feel more sexy when they are having their period.

cystitis (siss-*ty*-tiss)

The 'cyst' part of this word means bladder, 'itis' means disease or 'inflammation of'. Cystitis is an inflammation of the bladder and of the URETHRA. Those suffering from cystitis need to pee often and when they do they get an incredibly painful burning feeling although very little urine comes out. It's a very common illness which more than half of all women and many men will suffer from at some time in their life.

Cystitis can be caused by a number of things. Germs from the anus can easily get into the bladder and cause an infection. It can be a symptom of a SEXUALLY TRANSMITTED DISEASE or caused by an allergy to certain perfumed soaps, bath oils and vaginal deodorants. Sometimes cystitis is the result of internal bruising during SEXUAL INTERCOURSE, especially after the first time, which is why cystitis is sometimes called 'honeymoon disease'. Because the VAGINA and the urethra lie close together inside the female body, as the penis pushes in and out it can cause some bruising of the urethra which results in this infection. Stress or another illness entirely can also bring on an attack of cystitis, so it's by no means always related to sex.

Keeping your vagina or penis and anus really clean helps prevent cystitis, as does having sex in a different position so that the penis doesn't push against the urethra. Urinating immediately after sexual intercourse can also prevent it. If you do get an attack, drink lots of fluids like water, lemon barley water, cranberry juice, or marshmallow tea (from a herbalist) and soak in hot baths several times a day to ease the pain. A doctor will prescribe drugs to clear it up.

D

D & C See DILATATION AND CURETTAGES.

daisy chain

Slang for group sex involving a number of people all performing sex (vaginal, anal and/or oral) with the person in front and having it done to them by the person behind. The Latin term is *spirithriae.*

debauch

Borrowed from sixteenth-century French, this originally meant to SEDUCE someone's support away, or make them disloyal. In the seventeenth century the English puritan poet John Milton used the word to mean the seduction of someone from a virtuous or CHASTE way of life. Milton may have been preoccupied by the idea of debauchery because his first wife once left him to return to her family, which was on the opposite side to him in the English Civil War. As a supporter of Oliver Cromwell, Milton thought the Royalists were fairly immoral. Today, debauchery means extreme indulgence in SENSUAL pleasure.

deflower

This means to take someone's VIRGINITY away. In the fourteenth century it only referred to females, and also meant to violate or RAPE. Its present meaning doesn't imply rape any more, and it's used of males who lose their virginity as well as females.

dental dam

This is a small sheet of thin rubber latex used by dentists to protect the part of the mouth they're not working on. These latex barriers are also used during CUNNILINGUS to reduce the risk of spreading

SEXUALLY TRANSMITTED DISEASES. You place them over the VULVA before licking and KISSING your partner's GENITALS. Because they're so thin they needn't interfere with the pleasure of ORAL SEX.

Dental dams come in several sizes, colours and flavours (mint, for example) and you can buy them from surgical and dental supply companies. Some chemists are now beginning to stock them because they're increasingly used by couples who practise SAFER SEX.

desire

From the Old French for 'wish for', sexual desire is an urgent need for sexual pleasure and satisfaction (see ORGASM).

detumescence (de-*tyu*-mess-ence) See TUMESCENCE.

diaphragm (*di*-a-fram)

From the Greek word meaning barricade, diaphragm has several meanings. It is a dividing membrane or thin partition, the muscle wall that separates the lungs from the stomach which causes hiccups when it goes into spasm, and a CONTRACEPTIVE device, also called a CAP or Dutch cap.

It is a small, shallow bowl of thin rubber latex with a thicker rim of rubber-covered flexible wire. It's pushed into the VAGINA before SEXUAL INTERCOURSE and fits over the CERVIX. It works by blocking off the entrance to the WOMB to prevent SPERM from entering. However, the tiny sperms can get around the rim, and because diaphragms can get dislodged during lovemaking, they must be used with a SPERMICIDE. To make absolutely sure that all sperm are destroyed, the diaphragm must not be removed until eight hours after sex. Although they can be rather awkward and messy and can cause CYSTITIS, diaphragms have no dangerous side effects. They are as safe as CONDOMS in preventing PREGNANCY but do not prevent HIV or any other SEXUALLY TRANSMITTED DISEASE.

dick

First used by British soldiers, this has been slang for the PENIS since the middle of the nineteenth century. It may be shortened from 'derrick', an older slang word for the penis, or perhaps from rhyming slang 'creamstick' (see CREAM). As a verb, 'to dick' means to FUCK. 'Dickhead' is used to mean an incredibly stupid person – suggesting someone who can only use his SPERM cells because he doesn't have any brain cells.

There are several other male names which also mean penis – Jack, Peter, Percy, Willy, John Thomas, etc. Interestingly, apart from FANNY, there aren't any female names used for the VAGINA. This could be because boys, more than girls, are brought up to think of their sex organs as a friend (other oldish terms for penis include man, chap and fellow).

dilatation and curettage/dilatation and evacuation

Usually shortened to D & C or D & E, this is a standard operation performed on a woman to find out the causes of various problems in the WOMB such as bleeding, fibroids or CANCER. It is also an ABORTION method usually performed between the seventh and fourteenth week of pregnancy.

In a D & C the CERVIX is made larger (dilated) and the doctor pushes a long, thin metal instrument with a spoon-shaped end (curette) through the cervix into the womb to scrape out some of the lining which will include the FOETUS. It usually takes about five to fifteen minutes and is mostly done under a general anaesthetic which means you don't feel a thing.

A D & E involves the use of a narrow tube attached to a suction unit which empties (evacuates) the womb of its contents. This abortion method can be used up to the twenty-fourth week of pregnancy.

dildo

Sometimes spelt dildoe or dildol, this is an artificial PENIS-like object used by a woman or by her partner to massage her CLITORIS and to put into her VAGINA. The word probably comes from the Italian verb *diletto* meaning 'to delight', although it has been suggested that it comes from the word 'diddle-o' from an Old English word meaning 'to deceive or cheat'. The French call it *godemichet*, said to come from an Old French term for 'give me pleasure'.

There are historical records of dildos from ancient Greece when they were made either of wood or padded leather. It's thought that the following verse in the Old Testament refers to a dildo:

'Thou didst also take thy fair jewels of my gold and my silver, which I had given thee, and madest for thee images of men, and didst play the harlot with them . . .' (Ezekiel).

In the fifteenth century they were sometimes made, for a joke, in the shape of a nun – the head-dress of the nun (see TWAT) forming the GLANS or knob at the tip of the penis. The earliest mention of a dildo in English appears in a famous BAWDY poem, *The Choise of Valentines*, by Thomas Nashe (1567–1601). Today these sex toys tend to be made of plastic or latex rubber. If they have batteries in them to make them shake or vibrate, they're called vibrators.

Don Juan (jwahn or hwahn)
According to legend, Don Juan was a seventeenth-century Spanish nobleman from Seville. His name first appeared in a play called *El Burlador de Seville* by Gabriel Tellez who was writing under the name of Tirso de Molina. The Don SEDUCED, or more probably RAPED, the mayor's daughter and when challenged, killed the mayor. Some monks took revenge by luring him to their monastery where they killed him. To explain his disappearance the monks claimed that a statue of the mayor had come to life and sent Don Juan to hell.

In Mozart's famous opera *Don Giovanni*, which is based on this story, the Don is a troubled but lovable rogue who rapes, seduces and betrays women all around the world. Don Giovanni's servant reads out a long list of his sexual conquests to one of his master's female victims:

> Though my master provided the action,
> Just to write it gave me satisfaction . . .
>
> First, six hundred and forty Italians,
> Then the Germans with two battalions,
> French, one hundred and ninety,
> But the Spaniards number already
> One thousand and three.

The term 'Don Juan' came to be used with a sense of approval to describe a PROMISCUOUS or RANDY man. Psychologists, however, point out that the story shows a man with sexual and emotional problems, since he probably suffered from PREMATURE EJACULATION, and was totally incapable of forming permanent or meaningful relationships with women. He constantly has to prove his manhood through his sexual behaviour but is always left emotionally dissatisfied. This male neurosis is known as the Don Juan Syndrome and may be a sign of hidden HOMOSEXUALITY, since he tries so desperately to be a super-HETEROSEXUAL. (The pleasure Don Giovanni's servant gets from keeping a detailed list of his master's sexual activities suggests a form of VOYEURISM.)

Other slang terms for a promiscuous male include stud, CASANOVA, cocksman, COME (or cum) freak, gash hound, horndog, masher, meat-hound, rooster, stallion, studhammer, tomcat, woman-chaser, fast-worker, BAD dude, LOTHARIO, lounge lizard, make-out artist, Romeo, skirt-chaser, WOLF, PLAYBOY, womanizer.

Not all of them sound particularly complimentary but they're mostly used with a sense of approval. Any female who behaved in this way would immediately be called a NYMPHOMANIAC or a SLAG since, unlike men, women are expected to be CHASTE (see DOUBLE STANDARD).

dose

Since the 1860s this has been slang for a VENEREAL DISEASE, usually GONORRHOEA but sometimes SYPHILIS. The word itself comes from the Greek for 'giving' or 'gift' and has several non-slang senses: a dose of medicine or a drug is a measured amount of it; an added ingredient, water to wine for example, is called a dose; the word is also used for a short period of something you don't want or like, as in the phrases 'a dose of flu' or 'a dose of bad weather'. In the middle of the nineteenth century the expression 'to take a grown man's dose' meant a great deal of liquor – enough to make you drunk. It's possible that this phrase influenced the use of dose to mean gonorrhoea – too much of a good thing being something that you must pay for in the end. (Although you only need to have sex once with someone who is infected to get a SEXUALLY TRANSMITTED DISEASE.)

double standard

This term is used to describe the way one standard is applied to girls and women and a completely different (usually more favourable) one to boys and men. One obvious example is the way girls get called SLUTS, SLAGS, or worse, if they lose their VIRGINITY or express their sexual feelings. Boys, on the other hand, are almost expected to 'prove' their masculinity by sleeping around.

The main reason for a double standard in a society is the way in which MASCULINITY and FEMININITY are defined. Girls are brought up to be soft, gentle and passive while boys are brought up to be tough, aggressive and active. Research has shown that parents of tiny babies enourage girls to be quiet and still while they encourage boys to move about and explore their surroundings. It's thought to be 'natural' for boys to want to fight if they're angry and for girls just to sit and cry (preferably quietly). Change comes slowly but it does come. Only a few years ago it would have been almost inconceivable for a girl to say she wanted to be an engineer or for a boy to admit that he liked cooking. (Male chefs, of course, were an exception since they became the boss of the kitchen.) More and more people are questioning what we mean by the terms 'masculinity' and 'femininity' and demanding the sort of society where we all have an equal choice about who we are and how we behave.

douche (doosh)

From the French word meaning shower, a douche is a rubber bulb or bag with a tube coming out of it which is used to rinse out the VAGINA. The bag is filled with water or an antiseptic solution. It's used to help cure infections such as TRICHOMONIASIS or THRUSH. The tube is placed inside the vagina, and the bag held below waist-level and gently squeezed to push the contents out. Regular douching is not a good idea as it can upset the normal bacterial balance in the vagina and actually cause infections. But for someone already suffering from an infection a warm water and white vinegar douche may help restore the vagina to its healthy state. Douches are used more in the USA than in the UK where they're often called vaginal cleansing kits.

Some people think that a douche after SEXUAL INTERCOURSE will kill the sperm in the vagina and prevent pregnancy. Not only is this untrue, but the pressure of the fluid may actually help push the sperm further up into the UTERUS and make CONCEPTION more likely. The term 'douche-bag' is used, mostly by women, to insult a man they think is particularly weak or pathetic. It presumably suggests he isn't a 'real man', either because his SEMEN is a weak solution or that he's all empty bag and thin nozzle.

drag See CROSS-DRESSING.

droit du seigneur (dwah doo sen-*yer*)
This is French for 'right of the lord'. It was the right granted to the king, baron or lord of the manor in feudal times allowing him to DEFLOWER his female servants or serfs on the night before they married. It's a custom that dates back to ancient Egyptian times and only died out in Europe around the eleventh or twelfth century. Male bosses in the workplace who molest or sexually HARASS their young female employees behave as if they think droit du seigneur still exists. Fortunately, today these petty tyrants can be prosecuted.

Durex
The brand name for the most widely-used British CONDOM.

Dutch cap See DIAPHRAGM.

dyke
Sometimes spelled 'dike', this term for a LESBIAN appeared in the USA in the 1930s. No one knows where the word comes from although it has been suggested that it started as 'dite' from HERMAPH-RODITE. Dyke was originally a term of abuse used by prejudiced HETEROSEXUALS for a large masculine-looking lesbian stereotype (see BUTCH) or any woman who rejected male sexual advances. In recent years, lesbians have reclaimed the word for themselves with a sense of GAY pride.

dysmenorrhoea (dis-men-o-*ree*-a)

A medical term for painful PERIODS. The 'dys' part of this word implies 'difficult', 'meno' comes from the Greek word for 'monthly' referring to MENSTRUATION, and 'rrhoea' means 'to flow'. This pain, mainly in the lower abdomen or the small of the back, is something which most girls experience in ADOLESCENCE when they start having their periods. Other side-effects of having a period can include headaches, acne, cramps, mood changes, depression, nausea and water retention (areas such as the breasts often feel swollen and puffy). Most find that as they grow older many or all of these symptoms go away although some women experience a few of these symptoms throughout their menstruating lives.

Doctors don't know what causes dysmenorrhoea. There are various ways of relieving the symptoms. If aspirin, a hot-water bottle on the stomach or some cramp-reducing medicine or herbal tea don't help, a girl should see her doctor who may be able to prescribe a HORMONE pill (usually the CONTRACEPTIVE PILL), although this isn't recommended for very young teenage girls.

dyspareunia (dis-par-*oon*-ee-a)

This is the medical term for painful SEXUAL INTERCOURSE. In males it can be caused by inflammation of the FORESKIN. In females the problem can be anything from an inflammation of the VAGINA caused by an infection, to an unusually well-developed HYMEN, or an involuntary tightening of the muscles around the opening to the vagina which usually has a psychological cause (see VAGINISMUS). A girl or woman who suffers from dyspareunia may find intercourse is not only difficult and painful but physically impossible. It can happen as the result of fear or guilt, or because of an earlier, painful sexual experience such as RAPE. Ignorance or the clumsiness of her partner may also be the reason.

E

effeminate (ee-*fem*-in-et)

From the Latin meaning 'to become like a woman' this term is only used for males. This may seem obvious but given that all women are different and that some women are decidedly less FEMININE than others, it raises some interesting questions about what a woman is really like.

It hasn't always been bad for a man to be effeminate. In the sixteenth century for a man to be effeminate meant that he had gained qualities of gentleness, tenderness and compassion. But the 1611 English translation of the Bible translated the Latin word *effeminati* as 'SODOMITES' and the 1952 Revised Standard Version as 'male PROSTITUTES'. Today, to call a man effeminate is a way of saying that he's a WIMP or a sissy, probably hinting that he's a HOMOSEXUAL.

The famous American dictionary written by Noah Webster in 1828 defines effeminate as 'lacking in manly strength and purpose, exhibiting or proceeding from delicacy, weakness, emotionalism'. The latest edition of the equally famous *Oxford English Dictionary* gives the definition as 'womanish, unmanly, enervated, feeble, self-indulgent, voluptuous, unbecomingly delicate, or over-refined'.

It's all very confusing for people who want to be what they feel themselves to be rather than what society wants them to be like. There is clearly a DOUBLE STANDARD at work here. Definitions of MASCULINITY and femininity are constantly changing in small details and this depends on how each generation defines these two words. It is now becoming more acceptable for a man to be gentle and kind and for a woman to be strong and powerful.

egg cell

Every baby girl is born with two OVARIES which contain some hundreds of thousands of egg cells. After PUBERTY a single egg cell matures about once a month to form an OVUM which is then released from its ovary at OVULATION.

ejaculation (ee-jack-u-*lay*-shun)

From the Latin verb 'to throw out', ejaculation is the formal term for the sudden discharge of SEMEN from the PENIS when a male has an ORGASM. This can happen during SEXUAL INTERCOURSE, when he MASTURBATES or has a WET DREAM.

When a boy reaches PUBERTY, SPERMS are manufactured inside each of the two TESTICLES. They then move into an area just outside the testicles (but still inside the SCROTUM) called the EPIDIDYMIS, where they mature. This takes about six weeks. The next stage in their journey is through a tube called the vas deferens, or sperm duct. From here they move to the SEMINAL VESICLES where they get mixed with seminal fluid and are stored until he ejaculates. The name for the mixture of sperm and seminal fluid is SEMEN.

In order to ejaculate the male has to be sexually excited. This gives him an ERECTION and makes a valve inside the base of the penis close off the entry to the bladder so that no URINE can come out. At the highest point of excitement approximately 400 million tiny sperms in about two or three small spoonfuls of seminal fluid shoot up the URETHRA tube, which runs through the middle of the penis, and out of the tip. This process is known as ejaculation.

Other terms include to come (also used of women), to shoot one's load or wad, to pop one's cookies, and to get one's rocks off (which can also mean to have sexual intercourse).

Electra complex (ee-*lekt*-tra)

This psychological term is named after the mythological Greek princess who was the daughter of Queen Clytemnestra and King Agamemnon. Clytemnestra and her lover had Agamemnon murdered and then treated Electra as a slave and made sure she could never have children. With her brother Orestes, Electra plotted the death of her mother to avenge the murder of her father. Most scholars think Electra was an invention of the ancient Greek dramatist Euripedes.

The term was first used by Carl Jung, a disciple of Sigmund Freud, as a female equivalent of the OEDIPUS COMPLEX. Freud didn't agree with this view because he thought there were considerable differences between the development of female and male children. It's often used to describe women who are thought to be inappropriately dependent upon their fathers.

emasculate (ee-*mass*-kyu-late)

From the Latin word meaning CASTRATE, this literally means 'to remove the MASCULINITY', but it's mostly used in a figurative sense meaning to remove the strength or power of someone or something (such as a book or a movie) to make them weak and ineffective. (See also EFFEMINATE.)

embryo (*em*-bree-oh)

From the Greek word meaning 'to swell or grow', an embryo is a human in the very early stages of development from about the fourteenth day after the OVUM has been FERTILIZED (see ZYGOTE) until the fifty-fifth day after which it is called a FOETUS.

emergency contraception

If a girl or woman is afraid she might be PREGNANT because she had sex without using any CONTRACEPTION, because she forgot to take the PILL, the CONDOM split, or because she has been raped, there are two emergency methods that she can use. If she acts quickly, emergency contraception in the form of a pill or IUD, can usually prevent an unplanned pregnancy. Both these methods prevent a fertilized OVUM from attaching itself to the WOMB.

The first of two special doses of this pill, still widely called the 'morning-after pill', must be taken within the first three days after sex – the sooner the better. The second is taken twelve hours later. The IUD must be fitted within five days after sex – again, the sooner the better.

These pills can cause sickness and if a woman *is* sick she may need to return to her doctor or clinic for another one. The IUD is more effective (and can be kept in), but isn't suitable for everyone.

After taking these pills or having an IUD inserted she will get her PERIOD. These methods should only be used in a crisis situation and shouldn't be an excuse not to use regular BIRTH CONTROL methods.

endometriosis (en-doh-*mee*-tree-o-sis)

This is a painful condition which occurs when the tissue that normally forms the lining of the UTERUS or WOMB, begins to grow somewhere else in a woman's body. Its main symptom is painful PERIODS that may last a long time and be very heavy. (See also DYSMENORRHOEA.) Doctors treat endometriosis in a variety of ways. If it's a mild case they may suggest pain-killers. In more serious cases they may either prescribe the hormone PILL, which is normally used for CONTRACEPTION, or they may have to operate.

endometrium (end-o-*mee*-tree-um)

This is the medical term for the lining of the WOMB. It's what slips out of the VAGINA when a girl or woman has her PERIOD, and what nourishes the baby (see EMBRYO and FOETUS) as it develops during PREGNANCY.

english culture or vice See FLAGELLATION.

epididymis (eppy-*dih*-dih-mis)

Above each TESTICLE, inside the SCROTUM, lies a network of tiny tubes where the SPERM mature called the epididymis. If a boy or man gently feels his testicles when he's warm and relaxed, he will probably be able to separate the epididymis from the testicle. A boy should get to know how his testicles feel by checking them once a month so that he can find out if there any unusual lumps which may be a sign of CANCER.

erection

When a male has an erection his PENIS gets longer, wider and harder and stands away from his body. This is caused by a nerve centre at the base of the spinal cord which sends a message to make some blood rush into the veins and spongy tissue in his penis. The muscles inside the base of the penis then contract, preventing this extra blood from passing back out making the penis stiff. Although the penis is made only of blood vessels and tissue it feels as if there is a bone or something rigid inside when it's erect. The formal term is TUMESCENCE.

Erections are mostly the result of some sort of sexual stimulation such as being touched or having sexy thoughts. But during PUBERTY many boys find they get erections for no reason at all. These spontaneous erections are the result of high or changing levels of the hormone called TESTOSTERONE in their bodies. It can be very embarrassing to get an erection when it isn't wanted or expected, but this stops happening by the time he's a bit older and his hormone levels have settled down. Many boys and men wake up with an erection. This may be due to an EROTIC dream but it's more likely to be due to pressure from a full bladder. Spontaneous and morning erections will go away on their own.

Some diseases such as GONORRHOEA or leukaemia can cause a very painful condition, known as PRIAPISM, in which the penis stays erect all the time.

Slang terms for an erection include blue-veiner, bone, bone-on, bonk-on, on the bonk, hard-on, horn(y), prong-on, stiffy, stiff one. An early-morning erection is sometimes called a morning prouder or a piss proud.

erogenous zones

These are the sensitive parts of the body that give you good sexual feelings when they are touched, stroked, or KISSED. The word comes from Eros, the ancient Greek god of love and fertility. The most sexually exciting areas are the lips, the tongue, the CLITORIS and the GLANS or tip of the PENIS and prolonged stimulation can lead to an ORGASM. Most females and some males find that their nipples are also very sensitive. But everyone is different and finding out what areas of your partner's body turns them on when you touch them is an essential part of lovemaking, with or without PENETRATION.

erotica (ee-*rot*-ik-a)

Deriving its name from Eros, the ancient Greek male god of love and fertility, erotica is the name given to art, films and literature with a sexual theme that are often intended to arouse sexual feelings in the viewer or reader. It differs from PORNOGRAPHY, which is usually more explicit and thought to be OBSCENE rather than a work of art.

It's not always easy to tell the difference between the erotic and the pornographic – what is a work of art to one person may be obscene to someone else. Most people agree that the *Song of Solomon* in the Bible is a masterpiece of erotic poetry. But *La Maja*, the beautiful painting of a naked woman by the seventeenth-century Spanish artist Goya, was kept covered for years because many thought it was obscene. See also LADY CHATTERLEY'S LOVER.

eunuch (yoo-nuk)

Originally, this was a male slave in some Eastern and Middle Eastern countries who had had his TESTICLES removed and who guarded the women in the harem or was a chamberlain in a palace. It comes from two Greek words; the first meaning 'bed' and the second meaning 'to have charge of', making the literal meaning 'bedchamber guard'. See CASTRATION.

Informally, eunuch is also used as an insult to describe a boy or man who lacks so-called 'manly' qualities, or who is thought to be a bit weak and feeble. (See also EFFEMINATE and EMASCULATE.)

exhibitionism (ex-ib-*ish*-on-ism)

This is the technical term for the sexual PERVERSION widely called flashing. An exhibitionist is someone who gets a sexual kick out of exposing his or her GENITALS in public to someone else. The legal term is indecent exposure.

It's a crime committed mostly by men, most of whom have a limp penis when they expose themselves. They get their sexual satisfaction later in private when they MASTURBATE while remembering the incident. These men very seldom attack their victim. About five per cent have an ERECTION when they flash and these men can be dangerous. In situations like this you should run or be prepared to defend yourself by calling for help or anything else that feels right – it's probably best to trust your instincts. See also HARASSMENT.

extramarital sex (*mar*-rit-tal)
The formal term for ADULTERY meaning 'sex outside marriage'.

F

faeces (*fee*-sees)
From the Latin word meaning 'dregs', this is the formal term for the bodily waste which is discharged through the ANUS, also called excrement or shit. For most people it doesn't have much to do with sex (see COPROPHILIA), but it's one of the bodily fluids which can contain the HEPATITIS B virus or HIV. This means ANAL SEX is not part of SAFER SEX and anyone who has ANAL INTERCOURSE should always use a CONDOM – preferably a thicker one made specially for this purpose. The sexual activity called anilingus (tongue to anus) can also spread these viruses.

fag/faggot
A faggot, mostly shortened to fag, is an insulting slang term for a male HOMOSEXUAL. This can cause confusion in the UK where fag is also slang for a cigarette, possibly from the initials of the slogan 'For A Good Smoke' printed on cigarette tins sent to soldiers in France during the First World War (1914–1918).

There are several theories about the origins of fag. One is that during the 1920s cigarettes were thought to be less 'manly' than cigars. As the 'ette' part of any word suggests that something is feminine, a cigarette-smoking man was considered to be EFFEMINATE. Or it may come from the use of 'fag' at expensive British private schools for young boys who acted as servant/slave to one of the older boys and were (and still are) often pressured into homosexual relationships. Another theory is that it comes from Fagin, the name of a particularly nasty character in Charles Dickens' novel *Oliver Twist* who kept a gang of young boys to earn money for him by pick-pocketing.

The most likely source of the word is the use of 'faggot' for a woman, an insulting term for a flirty young woman. This would tie in with many other words meaning 'woman' used to abuse GAYS such as QUEEN, fairy, mary, nancy, pansy, daisy, femme, girl, nelly, sissy (short for sister).

fag hag

'Fag hag' is an abusive term for a woman who enjoys the company of GAY men. In the fourteenth century, a hag was an evil female spirit. The term then came to mean a witch and finally an ugly, nasty old woman. In the 1920s, a fag hag was British slang for a woman who smoked cigarettes. In the 1960s 'fag hag' got its current meaning. Other slang terms include 'fruit fly' and 'faggot's Moll'.

fairy See PANSY.

fake orgasm

If a girl or woman pretends to have an ORGASM, it's called 'faking it'. She might do this because she thinks she 'ought' to have one or because her partner doesn't know how to get her sexually aroused. Good sex is not about scoring orgasms and it isn't essential to reach orgasm every time, but if a woman's partner hasn't found out how she likes to be touched and kissed before he has his orgasm (see FOREPLAY) she won't feel very satisfied. Faking an orgasm doesn't help her or her partner discover how to really enjoy sex.

Fallopian tubes

Named after the sixteenth-century Italian anatomist Gabriel Fallopio, these two tubes are part of the female internal reproductive organs. Each Fallopian tube is joined to the upper part of the WOMB at one end, while the other end lies close to an OVARY and has a fringed funnel that looks a bit like a sea anemone. This collects the OVUM which is dispatched from one or other of the ovaries about every twenty-eight days (see OVULATION). The ovum then travels down the Fallopian tube to the womb. CONCEPTION takes place in a Fallopian tube.

family planning

This term means CONTRACEPTION or birth control, especially when this is applied to the regulation of family size and the space between births of children. In the UK, the Family Planning Association runs clinics in many towns and cities which give advice and help on contraception, EMERGENCY CONTRACEPTION, pregnancy testing, pregnancy and ABORTION and other aspects of sex and health. Consult the phone book to find your local branch. See also COUNSELLING.

fanny

In the UK it's often used by young girls as a friendly term for their external sex organs (see GENITALS, VULVA and CUNT). In the USA a fanny is slang for the buttocks (see ASS/ARSE).

The American term may have come from the word 'fundament', a thirteenth-century term for the buttocks. In the British sense the word probably comes from the novel by John Cleland and published in 1749, which was originally called *Memoirs of a Woman of Pleasure* but usually known as *Fanny Hill*. The story is about a fifteen-year-old country girl who is rescued from a BROTHEL by a handsome young man. They fall in love but when he is sent overseas, Fanny becomes a high-class PROSTITUTE and a MISTRESS to various wealthy men. After many sexy adventures it all ends happily ever after when Fanny and her true-love meet up again. The moral of the story is that sex is fun but shared love is even better. The book is definitely EROTIC although it doesn't contain a single OBSCENE word. This hasn't stopped it from being banned in most countries at one time or other for being PORNOGRAPHIC. There is also a reference to fanny in a Shakespearean play. In a passage rich with puns and *double entendres* (see Glossary), in *Romeo and Juliet* the old Nurse enters and asks Peter for her fan. Mercutio cheekily replies, 'Good Peter, to hide her face; for her fan's the fairer face.' However, it is likely that Shakespeare used it to refer to her buttocks, as the play was written in 1596, long before the word had its current meaning.

fantasy

The Greek word, from which we get the word fantasy, literally means 'to present to the mind' or to imagine. Sexual fantasies are EROTIC day-dreams which we mostly recognize to be unreal or difficult, if not impossible, to achieve. Most children forget, or repress, their sexual fantasies perhaps because in our society children are not encouraged to think of themselves as sexual beings. By the time we reach ADOLESCENCE we become more aware of ourselves as sexual beings and our fantasy life can become very rich. Fantasies can be a powerful means of sexual excitement and most people draw upon their innermost dreams and memories when they MASTURBATE and often when they make love.

There are no limits to the power of the human imagination and we sometimes fantasise about the most improbable things. You may find yourself having erotic thoughts or dreams about someone you fancy (this word comes from the same root as fantasy). It's quite natural to imagine yourself having sex with someone of the same sex or with someone who you wouldn't dream of having sex with in real life. It's also completely normal to have violent or extreme fantasies such as being or going with a prostitute, or about raping someone or being raped. The main point about fantasies is that we should be in control of them – we choose our fantasy partners and can stop them when we want.

felch

Also called 'velch' and 'fletch', this is the mostly GAY sexual practice of EJACULATING into the ANUS of a partner and then sucking the SEMEN out.

fellatio (fell-art-ee-o)

From the Latin word for sucking, fellatio is a form of ORAL SEX involving the KISSING, licking and sucking of the PENIS to give (and receive) sexual pleasure. In the nineteenth century it was one of the sexual practices which was banned under the legal description of SODOMY. But the famous American sex researcher Dr Alfred Kinsey (1894–1956) discovered that fellatio was an accepted practice amongst most married couples – either as a part of FOREPLAY or as a way of avoiding pregnancy.

If the man has an ORGASM while his penis is being sucked he will EJACULATE into the mouth of his partner – something which some people like and others don't. SEMEN itself is not harmful but may contain HIV which leads to AIDS. Saliva can also carry this virus. HERPES is another infection which can be passed from mouth to genitals. Couples practising SAFER SEX should use a CONDOM if they have fellatio. Some imaginative manufacturers make condoms in various different flavours to make it more fun.

Slang terms for fellatio include BLOW JOB, French job, gob-job, head job, knob job, giving head, deep throat (after a 1970s pornographic movie of this name starring Linda Lovelace), gamarouche/gameroosh (a nineteenth-century term possibly of French or Arabic origin), plating (shortened from 'plate of ham', rhyming slang for 'gam' from gameroosh), face fucking, lipstick on a dipstick, sixty-eight ('you suck me and I'll owe you one'). See also SOIXANTE-NEUF.

fem/femme (fem)

These two words – pronounced in the same way – used to mean a girl or woman, from the French word *femme* meaning 'woman'. Today they're mostly used for the more feminine, or passive, partner in a HOMOSEXUAL or LESBIAN relationship. Not that every GAY relationship automatically has one partner who is dominant and one who is passive. Like any type of relationship some couples achieve equality by changing roles or by neither taking a dominant role.

A *femme sole*, from the French meaning 'solitary woman' is a legal term for a single woman, widow, or divorced or legally-separated woman. Another French term, *femme fatale*, literally meaning 'disastrous woman', is used for a mysterious and SEDUCTIVE woman, a siren who lures men into dangerous and compromising situations.

female condom

This CONTRACEPTIVE device is a cross between a DIAPHRAGM and a CONDOM and often goes by its trade name, 'Femidom'. It's a loose-fitting, soft, thin, polyurethane (plastic) sheath that is placed inside the VAGINA where it lines the contours of the vaginal walls. Inside the closed end is a springy ring to help fit the Femidom inside and anchor it round the CERVIX. At the open end (which stays outside the vagina, resting on the LABIA) there is another springy ring which stops it from slipping up into the vagina and through which the PENIS goes. The Femidom is already lubricated to make it easier to insert but it may need extra lubricating jelly to make it more comfortable for the penis.

Due to its recent release, it's too soon to know how effective the female condom is at preventing pregnancy, but it promises to be as effective as the male condom and possibly even better at preventing the spread of SEXUALLY TRANSMITTED DISEASES, including HIV which can cause AIDS.

Couples who have tested the Femidom say that it doesn't look very attractive and it's also quite difficult to place into position initially, but that this becomes easier after some practice. If it works well it will be a good method of birth control and SAFER SEX for women who like to be in control of their own bodies. Femidoms are available from chemists, but they are presently three times more expensive than a condom.

Femidom See FEMALE CONDOM.

feminine

The Latin word *femina*, meaning 'woman', comes from an even older root word meaning 'the suckling one' or 'the sucked one' suggesting a very simplistic definition of a woman as one who breast-feeds. When 'feminine' first entered the English language in the fourteenth century it only meant 'female'. By the sixteenth century when a strong woman, Elizabeth I, was on the throne, it implied weakness. To many, it still does.

Over the centuries definitions of femininity have changed. Women themselves have proved that femininity doesn't have to mean weak, passive, dominated and feeble. A woman can still be feminine, whether she is a company director or a truck driver. See also MASCULINE.

fertilization

From the Latin word meaning 'to carry' or 'to bear', fertilization is the name given to the process where the female OVUM and the male SPERM cell unite to form a new life. Fertilization takes place in the FALLOPIAN TUBE after SEXUAL INTERCOURSE has taken place or, if for some reason either partner is infertile or finds it difficult to conceive, scientists can fertilize the egg in a laboratory in a process known as *in vitro* which literally means 'in glass', often shortened to IVF for *in vitro* fertilization. Following this, the fertilized egg is then placed into the woman's WOMB. Babies conceived in this way have become known as 'test-tube' babies.

fetish

From the Latin word meaning 'artificial', fetish originally meant an object worshipped in early societies which was thought to have magical powers. Today, we use the word in general terms to mean an object or activity that people get obsessed about, so you might say, 'she or he makes a fetish of getting up early'. In a psychological or sexual sense it means an object or part of the body which some-one, called a fetishist, focuses on in order to get sexual satisfaction (see PERVERSION). She or he is able to relate only to this object (such as high-heel shoes or RUBBER clothing) or part of the human body (such as the female breasts or ankles) and not to another person as a whole. This means they can't enjoy a full and loving relationship.

fingerfucking

This rather blunt term means to stimulate a girl or woman by pushing a finger into her VAGINA. If she is a VIRGIN it means that her HYMEN (if she has one) gets broken. Other slang terms meaning the same thing are: to diddle, to finger, to FRIG, to play stink-finger or stinky-pinky. Everyone's GENITALS can smell unpleasant if they aren't washed regularly, but these last terms are two of many negative words and expressions which suggest that some men have problems with a woman's natural smell.

fistfucking

A sexual practice which involves ANAL PENETRATION with a closed fist. This can be a dangerous practice, as anal penetration can rupture the delicate anal membranes. It is also not recommended as a SAFER SEX practice.

flagellation (flaj-ell-*a*-shon)
This is the practice of whipping or beating someone for sexual purposes. It is a PERVERSION. People who enjoy receiving it are called MASOCHISTS; those who get turned on by doing the whipping are called SADISTS. Those who enjoy both are called SADO-MASOCHISTS. In early Christian and medieval times self-flagellation was practised as a form of religious worship – people who did it probably got aroused to states of religious ecstacy. Many PROSTITUTES offer this service, which is usually referred to as 'discipline'. A slang term for it is 'fladge'. See also SPANKING.

flasher See EXHIBITIONISM.

flirt
In its original sense this meant 'to flick or move something quickly and suddenly'. In the sixteenth century it was a term to describe a 'flighty woman'. Shakespeare used the word 'flirt-gill' to mean a WANTON woman, an unserious wench. (Gill was short for Gillian, a girl's name which was used as a general term for a sexually attractive or available young woman.) By the eighteenth century 'flirt' was used by Samuel Richardson, the British author of several early erotic novels, to mean a woman who offers playful, insincere sexual invitations. In 1755, the lexicographer (see Glossary) Samuel Johnson defined it as 'a woman of loose, giddy or flighty character; a pert young hussy'. Today, a flirt is someone of either sex who behaves in an amorous way to signal that they're sexually attracted to someone else.

foetus (*fee*-tuss)
From a Latin word meaning 'offspring' the unborn child in the WOMB is referred to as a foetus from the eighth week of PREGNANCY.

foreplay
This is the act of sexually arousing your partner before SEXUAL

INTERCOURSE. Finding out how your partner's body responds to KISSING, stroking, licking, sucking and caressing is an important part of lovemaking. Our lips, mouths and GENITALS are particularly sexually responsive, but everyone has different parts of their body (called EROGENOUS ZONES) which respond to being touched.

Foreplay is particularly important for females since they can take longer to become sexually aroused than males. When a woman is sexually aroused, her VAGINA is more likely to produce a fluid (see LUBRICATION) which makes it easier – and more pleasurable – for the penis to enter her vagina.

The term foreplay implies that lovemaking always ends in intercourse. But PENETRATION is only one way of enjoying sex. All the kissing and touching, which is traditionally thought of as foreplay, can be just as satisfying, especially if both partners reach ORGASM. The added attraction for those practising SAFER SEX is that there is virtually no risk of transmitting HIV through foreplay (provided neither partner has any cuts or open sores on their body). See also AFTERPLAY.

foreskin

This is the protective fold of thickish skin tissue that covers the GLANS, or rounded head of the PENIS, when the penis is in its normal state. The technical term for it is PREPUCE. When the penis is ERECT the foreskin gets pulled right back and is barely noticeable. Some boys have their foreskin removed for religious or hygienic reasons or because the foreskin is too tight, in an operation called CIRCUMCISION.

fornication

This means SEXUAL INTERCOURSE between consenting unmarried people and it can also mean ADULTERY. The word has an interesting history which goes back to an Indo-European root word (see Glossary) meaning 'warm'. This root gave the ancient Greeks their word for 'hot' – from which we get our words thermometer, thermal and thermonuclear. The same root gave the Romans the Latin word *fornax* meaning an oven, from which we get our word 'furnace', and *fornix* meaning 'vault' or 'arch', probably from the shape of some of the ovens or kilns used by the Romans. *Fornix* then came to be used as the name for the underground vaults in Rome which were rented out cheaply to the poor and to PROSTITUTES. Eventually *fornix* came to mean BROTHEL and *fornatrix* to mean prostitute. The masculine version of the word was *fornicator*, which was a man who paid to have sex with prostitutes. The activity between a *fornatrix* and a *fornicator* became known, in English, as fornication.

four-letter word

This term refers to words generally considered offensive and OB-SCENE that describe the female and male GENITALS, sexual activity, and other bodily functions. The strange thing about four-letter words is that they don't all have four letters – BUGGER for instance – although several of the more common ones such as FUCK, CUNT, piss and shit do.

Many people have a shocked reaction to these words because they are taught that they are obscene and should never be used. But, over the years, words thought to be obscene pass in and out of fashion. Cunt, for instance, was a perfectly acceptable term for the female genitals until about the fifteenth century when it became TABOO; from 1700 until the 1960s it was actually banned from books. PENIS, on the other hand, has never been considered a four-letter word. However, there are other words for penis, such as prick, which are considered to be obscene.

French culture/kiss/letter

For some reason the British seem to think that French people have a lot of ORAL SEX when they make love. If an English PROSTITUTE advertises that she offers 'French culture' it means that she performs FELLATIO. When a couple give each other oral sex at the same time (fellatio and CUNNILINGUS), it's known as SOIXANTE-NEUF, which is French for 'sixty-nine'. 'French abortion' is slang for spitting out the SEMEN after fellatio. A FRENCH KISS is when the tongue is pushed deep inside the partner's mouth. No one knows why the French are supposed to be the experts at oral sex as it is performed by couples all around the world.

There are some 'French' terms which don't involve oral sex – some of them suggesting fear of the foreigner just across the English Channel rather than envy of their sexuality. 'French disease' or 'French gout' are obsolete (see Glossary) terms for SYPHILIS. A 'French letter' is a CONDOM; A 'French tickler' is a condom with soft petal-like bits at the open end which supposedly give more pleasure to the woman. A 'frenchie' is American slang for a condom. French people, meanwhile, have retaliated by calling a condom a *capote anglaise*, which translates as English cloak or hood.

frig

From the Latin word *fricare* meaning 'to rub', frig first became part of the English language in 1590 when it meant to MASTURBATE, often referring to female masturbation, hence the obsolete word (see Glossary) 'fricatrice' meaning LESBIAN. In the nineteenth century, the expression 'Frig it!' was often used in the same sense as 'Fuck it!'. People confused these two exclamations and, as a result, frig came to mean SEXUAL INTERCOURSE. In the USA, frig and frigging are swear-words thought to be slightly less offensive than fuck (see FOUR-LETTER WORD) and they also mean FINGERFUCKING. In the UK frig is still sometimes used in its early sense of masturbate, as in the phrase 'stop frigging about'.

frigid (*frij*-id)

This comes from the Latin word for 'cold' (from which we also get the word refrigerator). It's popularly used to mean a girl or woman who either doesn't feel like having sex or who doesn't have an ORGASM. But in both of these cases it might simply be that she doesn't fancy the boy or man in question or that he didn't know how to get her properly sexually aroused during FOREPLAY.

Frigidity in its true psychosexual sense is a fairly rare condition which ranges from a lack of sexual feeling or pleasure (known as sexual anaesthesia) to an active and total aversion to sexual relations. There are many possible causes, including sexual ABUSE in child-hood, inhibitions picked up from her parents' attitudes towards sex, fear of PREGNANCY or of SEXUALLY TRANSMITTED DISEASE, a sense of guilt, and hostility towards males. It can also be the result of a physical inability to have SEXUAL INTERCOURSE (see VAGINISMUS).

frottage (frott-*ahj*)

From the French verb for 'to rub' this is the PERVERSE behaviour of men who get sexual pleasure from rubbing against or playing with women's clothing or from rubbing up against strangers (usually females) in public places. Men who HARASS women in this way are called frotteurs.

Frotteurs don't expose their GENITALS like FLASHERS do, and they seldom want to do anything dangerous, but it is still a very unpleasant form of sexual harassment for any girl or woman.

An old term for frotteurism, one still used by British police, is 'bustle-punching'.

frustration

Originating from the Latin for 'in vain', which is related to another word meaning 'fraud', sexual frustration is the disappointment experienced when sexual DESIRE is aroused but not satisfied. Females may experience a throbbing pain in their GENITAL area if they are frustrated in their efforts to have an ORGASM. Males may feel a pain in their TESTICLES known as 'BLUE BALLS' or 'love nuts'.

fuck

This can mean to COPULATE, the act of copulation, the sexual partner in the act of copulation, and the ejaculated SEMEN. It's also used as a swear word in a variety of ways.

There are several theories about where this word comes from. Some have suggested the Sanskrit word (see Glossary) for 'bull' or the Cantonese word *fook* meaning happiness. Another theory is that naval commanders in the early nineteenth century used it as an abbreviation for 'For Unlawful Carnal Knowledge' in their logbooks – but this is highly unlikely since 'fuck' as a verb has been in use since 1503.

'Fuck' was originally Standard English (see Glossary). But this didn't stop it from becoming one of the best-known FOUR-LETTER

WORDS in the English language. The great literary masters James Joyce and D.H. Lawrence (see LADY CHATTERLEY'S LOVER) tried unsuccessfully to restore 'fuck' to its original dignified use in their novels. However, their books were initially banned or censored because of the inclusion of this and other four-letter words. It was omitted from most dictionaries until the 1960s.

Since the nineteenth century, 'fuck' has been used as a noun to mean the act of SEXUAL INTERCOURSE, or a person (usually the woman) viewed as a SEX OBJECT, as in the phrase 'She's a good fuck'. In response to this, many women have claimed the word for their own use and you now hear women describing a man as a good or bad fuck. For many people, however, a woman who uses this word is not thought to be very FEMININE and certainly not 'lady-like'.

Slang words for having sex include bang, boff, BONK, bop, hump, knock off, nail, pluck, poke, pop, pound, prong, pump, SCREW, shaft, tear off a piece, and to cut a slice off the joint (see MEAT). Many slang words are euphemisms (see Glossary) that people tend to use in certain social situations. Examples of this are dip one's wick, get laid (see LAY), get one's ashes hauled, get one's banana peeled, get into her pants, get one's nuts cracked, get one's leg over, get one's rocks off, get stuffed, have one's end off, play hide-the-weenie, lay the pipe, and perform. Terms which emphasize that sex can be about love, tenderness or mutual pleasure for both women and men are to MAKE LOVE, to BALL, to boogie, to do it, nookie, to party, to sleep with someone, and go to bed with someone.

G

gamete (*gam*-eet)
Based on the Greek word for 'marriage' (BIGAMY has the same root), this is the technical term for a sex cell (see OVUM and SPERM).

gang-bang/rape
A gang-bang, also called 'gang shay' and 'gang shag', is when several males take it in turns to have SEXUAL INTERCOURSE with one girl or woman, with her consent. Gang RAPE means the woman does not give her consent.

gardnerella
Gardnerella vaginalis is a bacterial infection of the vagina often accompanied by ANAEROBIC VAGINOSIS. The infection may be SEXUALLY TRANSMITTED or triggered by something like a TAMPON or fingers, which can introduce the bacteria into the VAGINA.

Symptoms include a watery, greyish, fishy-smelling discharge from the vagina. It can be cured by antibiotics. Girls or women who are sexually active should also make sure their partner(s) go to the doctor or SPECIAL CLINIC since they, too, may be infected. A CONDOM should be used during sex until it has been cured.

gay
The original meaning of 'gay' as 'merry and bright', has been extended to also mean someone who is HOMOSEXUAL. The word 'gay' has a long history connecting it to homosexuality.

When 'gay' first entered the English language in the thirteenth century it meant 'full of joy or mirth, light-hearted, exuberantly cheerful, sportive, merry'. A 'gay girl' was a female child, a 'knave girl' was a male child – 'girl' in those days meant a child of either sex. By the nineteenth century a 'gay girl' was a PROSTITUTE and a 'gaying instrument' meant a PENIS. In the 1920s the term 'gay boy' emerged in Australia to mean a male homosexual. Around the same time female and male homosexuals in the USA adopted the word gay with a sense of self-irony. But by the 1960s the slogan 'glad to be gay' indicated that the word was used with some self-confidence and pride by homosexuals. Since the 1970s many female homosexuals have preferred to call themselves LESBIAN since the word 'gay' to them suggested a male. See also QUEER.

geld (with a hard 'g')

This comes from a Norse word meaning 'BARREN.' Although it can refer to human male CASTRATION, to the removal of the TESTICLES from a male and of the OVARIES from a female, it's mostly used today to mean the castration of male animals. Female animals are spayed.

gender (*jen*-der)

People and animals are divided into two genders – the female sex and the male sex. 'Gender' can be used in this sense but it has become more widely used to mean FEMININITY and MASCULINITY. We're all born with the relevant CHROMOSOMES, HORMONES and hormone-producing glands (OVARIES or TESTICLES) that determine whether we're female or male. But gender in the sense of femininity and masculinity is something we learn. Gender is also a term used by language experts to describe how some languages are organized (see Glossary).

gene (jeen)

Based on a Greek word meaning 'beget, produce', a gene is a unit of DNA (deoxyribonucleic acid) which is contained in the central nucleus of every living cell. The genes in a CHROMOSOME control the physical characteristics such as hair and eye colour and are passed down from one generation to the next.

genitals (*jen*-ee-tals)

From the Latin word for 'beget', which means to procreate or reproduce a child, this is the formal term for the external organs of the reproductive system. The outer female genitals, or VULVA, consist of the CLITORIS, the outer and inner LABIA (also called lips), and the opening to the VAGINA. The male outer genitals consist of the PENIS and the SCROTUM which contain the TESTICLES. In plural form the Latin 'genitalia' is sometimes used.

gigolo (*jig*-oh-lo)

This word is the masculine version of the French word *gigole*, a dance-hall woman. Originally, a gigolo was a professional male dancing-partner or escort. Presumably reflecting what often happened to gigolos, the word then came to mean a man who was paid by his female client to have sex with her. Although he's clearly a male PROSTITUTE, 'gigolo' is widely used to mean any young man who makes himself attractive to older women.

glamour

In the fourteenth century this word used to be spelled *gramayre*, meaning learning or grammar. A hundred years later it referred to occult or supernatural learning and was associated with witches. By the end of the fifteenth century it meant an evil charm that people believed was cast by a witch on men, which made them think that their PENIS had disappeared. For this 'crime' thousands of elderly, confused and usually single women were tortured and burned to death throughout Europe and America.

As belief in witches faded the word dropped out of use. It was reintroduced by writer Sir Walter Scott (1771–1832), who used its Scottish spelling, 'glamour', with the meaning of a harmless magic spell. By the mid-nineteenth century, glamour had developed the sense of the delusive and alluring charm used by women to attract men.

In the twentieth century 'glamour magazine' was an early term for one which printed photos of sexy female film stars who bewitched their audiences. It is now used to describe someone or something that has an alluring and exciting beauty or charm.

glans

From the Latin word meaning 'acorn', this is the name for the rounded top part of the CLITORIS and of the PENIS.

golden shower See URINE.

gonads (with a hard 'g')

From the Greek word meaning 'procreation' and 'seed', this is the medical term for the female OVARIES and male TESTICLES. They are also called the primary sex glands.

gonorrhoea (goh-noh-*ree*-ah)

The name of this SEXUALLY TRANSMITTED DISEASE was invented in 130 AD by the ancient Greek physician, Galen, from the words for 'seed' and 'flow'. One of its main symptoms in males is a discharge from the PENIS – although it isn't the seed or SPERM that actually flows out. It's a disease that's been around for thousands of years and is referred to in the Old Testament in the Book of Leviticus.

Gonorrhoea can only be spread by vaginal or ANAL SEX or by ORAL SEX. You can't catch it from doorknobs, bed linen, clothes, toilet seats, towels or swimming pools. Very occasionally a child-carer with acute gonorrhoea may transfer the germs on their hands (from their GENITALS) to a baby's sex organs.

Many people, especially females, have no symptoms at all with this disease. It therefore spreads all too easily since people don't always realize that they have it. If your partner has it, it's almost certain that you will too. If symptoms do occur they usually show up from one day to two weeks after contact. Females may get a whitish, greenish or yellowish unpleasant-smelling discharge from their VAGINA and also from their ANUS. It hurts when they pee. They get a pain in the lower part of their abdomen, and a sore throat or swollen glands. Males will probably get a discharge from their penis which sometimes drips all the time, a discharge from their anus, a burning, itching pain when they pee, and a sore throat or swollen glands.

If untreated, gonorrhoea can lead to serious complications such as STERILITY and blindness. Both partners, even if they have no symptoms, should go to see a doctor or go to a SPECIAL CLINIC which deals with sexually transmitted diseases. The doctor will prescribe penicillin, usually with another drug. Because at least twenty-five per cent of people with gonorrhoea also have a disease called CHLAMYDIA, this should be tested for as well. You must not have sex until you are completely cured – not even using CONDOMS which, although better than nothing, aren't very reliable as a means of preventing reinfection.

Slang terms include the CLAP, a DOSE, the drip, morning dew, gleet, hot piss, and the whites.

Gräfenberg spot

Also called the G-spot for short, this is a sensitive area that lies inside the female body just outside the front wall of the VAGINA, between the back of the pubic bone and the CERVIX. It takes its name from the German physician Dr Ernst Gräfenberg. He was the first to describe this area that swells when pressure is put on it during sex, either by the PENIS or by a partner's fingers and which, during her ORGASM, gives a woman a sudden flow of fluid from the URETHRA.

Some women feel as if they are peeing and it may also explain why so many people believe that women EJACULATE when they come. But there is great debate amongst sex researchers about whether the G-spot really exists. It may be simply that some women produce more lubrication from the walls of their vagina during orgasm than others, or that some women feel so relaxed during their orgasm that a small amount of pee does escape down the urethra. Either way female orgasms can be just as satisfying with or without this sudden flow.

H

hand job/relief

A hand job is slang for MASTURBATION which originally meant 'to defile by hand'. It usually means self-masturbation but is also used for when a lover does it to a partner. Hand relief, or relief massage, are both euphemisms (see Glossary) often used by MASSAGE PARLOURS to describe one of the services that the masseuses provide for their clients.

harassment

This word comes from an Old French word meaning 'to set a dog on'. Over the years it has come to mean something considerably less violent, a process in language known as amelioration (see Glossary). Sexual harassment is the general term used to describe the behaviour of someone (usually male) who continually troubles or annoys someone else (usually female) for their own sexual pleasure and always without the woman's consent. Anything more serious is called INDECENT assault, INCEST or RAPE. Technically speaking, unless physical contact is involved, sexual harassment isn't a crime. However, the victim will often feel quite seriously upset or intimidated.

This is why it's important to report any kind of sexual harassment. Not everyone feels particularly bothered by it, but if the harasser isn't stopped he may do it to someone else who it seriously disturbs. It's not always easy to report someone who is sexually harassing you – especially if it's a teacher, employer or someone you or your family know well. It's also a good idea to talk it over with a sympathetic friend or an adult you trust, as well as someone who is professionally trained to help in such situations (see COUNSELLING).

For different forms of harassment, see EXHIBITIONISM (also called

FLASHING), FROTTAGE, MOLESTING, KERB CRAWLING, OBSCENE PHONE CALLS, VOYEURISM and WOLF-WHISTLE.

harlot

This is a rather old-fashioned word for a PROSTITUTE or WHORE. When it was first borrowed from the Old French in the thirteenth century it meant 'a rascally rogue or knave' as well as 'a jester or juggler'. By the fifteenth century 'harlot' was no longer used to refer to men. It meant a female prostitute – but it had a slight aristocratic ring to it because it was (wrongly) supposed that the word came from Arlette, the name of the mother of William the Conqueror, who had previously been known as William the BASTARD.

hepatitis

From the Latin word *hepar*, this is an inflammation of the liver caused by two viruses called hepatitis A, which is not a SEXUALLY TRANSMITTED DISEASE, and hepatitis B, a much more serious infection which can be sexually transmitted. The B virus is found in the blood, saliva and FAECES of an infected person and can be spread by ANAL SEX, by ORAL SEX and by sharing the needles and syringes of someone with the virus. Symptoms include vomiting, fatigue, depression and jaundice and can lead to permanent damage of the liver resulting in death. It is especially dangerous for those with HIV.

About ten per cent of people with hepatitis B show no symptoms but are carriers of the virus. A simple blood test can be done at a SPECIAL CLINIC to show if the infection is present. There is no cure, but someone who thinks they might be at risk can be vaccinated against it.

hermaphrodite

This is an animal or plant that has both female and male reproductive organs. It gets its name from an ancient Greek myth. Hermaphroditus was the son of Aphrodite, goddess of love (see APHRODISIAC), and Hermes, god of fine-talking and messenger to all the other goddesses and gods. One day Hermaphroditus arrived at the fountain of the nymph, Salmacis, who fell in love with him at first sight.

Unfortunately, as she tried to embrace him, he drowned in her waters. Salmacis was distraught and begged the goddesses and gods to bring him back to life and unite them for ever. This they did and, according to the Greeks, the two lovers became the first hermaphrodite.

Apart from some rare malformed babies who are born with an OVARY and a TESTIS (both of which are INFERTILE), true hermaphroditism in humankind is mythical since no human can make themselves pregnant. Nearly all so-called human hermaphrodites are people with the wrong number of CHROMOSOMES. See also ANDROGYNY.

herpes (her-pees)

The word herpes comes from the Greek word 'to creep' presumably because of the rather mysterious way in which this virus, called herpes simplex virus (HSV) apparently travels from the mouth to the VAGINA, PENIS or ANUS. There are two types of herpes viruses: HSV I, which produces cold sores or fever blisters on the face (usually lips and mouth), and HSV II, which involves sores in the GENITAL area. Both types of this virus can affect both areas.

The two different viruses probably cross over as a result of ORAL SEX, although it's possible for herpes to be spread if a person first touches the cold sore on their mouth and then touches their vagina or penis. It can also be passed from vagina to penis or penis to vagina by having SEXUAL INTERCOURSE with someone who has a herpes sore on his or her genitals.

The genital sores develop crusts which may ooze a bit for three to four days. They then form scabs and heal on their own. HSV is at its most infectious from the time the sores crust over and probably for the next day or two.

Most sufferers find the first attack is the worst, sometimes accompanied by a temperature and flu-like symptoms. Most girls or women with HSV II develop sores on both the vagina and the CERVIX during the first infection and the virus is implicated in cervical CANCER. Only a small percentage of people suffer further attacks. Any subsequent attacks – often triggered by stress, illness, MENSTRUATION or pregnancy – are usually much milder than the first.

As yet there is no cure for herpes, but it's worth going to your doctor because a drug can be prescribed which helps minimize the symptoms of subsequent attacks. Washing the genital area in salty water, keeping cool and wearing cotton underwear (or none at all) and a mild painkiller all help to relieve the pain. Kissing and oral sex should be avoided if either you or your partner has a cold sore or fever blister on your mouth. Intercourse, even with a condom, while either of you has a herpes sore on your genitals, is particularly unwise.

heterosexual

From the Greek word meaning 'other' or 'different', a heterosexual is a person whose sexual interest is focussed on the opposite sex. It's thought that around fifty per cent of people are heterosexual, about ten per cent are HOMOSEXUAL, and forty per cent are BISEXUAL.

GAYS sometimes use the slang term 'straight' for someone who is heterosexual – perhaps in revenge for the use of 'BENT', which implies criticism of homosexuals. 'Straight' isn't a particularly complimentary term since it suggests all heterosexuals are boringly upright and inflexible in their behaviour or thoughts. As well as the informal 'hetero', another slang term is 'right-handed', presumably because left-handedness is widely thought to be less 'normal'. American slang for a heterosexual man includes breeder, citizen, and VANILLA.

hickey

This used to mean a pimple or a skin blemish. The word was then used for a rich dessert, presumably because rich, sweet food encourages pimples. Hickey is now widely used in the USA for what's called a LOVE-BITE in the UK.

HIV

HIV stands for Human Immunodeficiency Virus. If this virus gets into a person's bloodstream, it will begin to attack the white blood cells. These cells form part of the body's immune system and help prevent diseases. HIV enters the white blood cells and makes them produce more of the virus which eventually kills the white blood cells. Eventually there are not enough of these cells to protect the body from infection.

The majority of people with HIV infection show no signs of illness and look and feel perfectly healthy. Some, shortly after becoming infected, may experience night sweats, swollen glands, weight loss, a persistent cough and general flu-like symptoms. Others may develop more serious symptoms, such as swelling of glands in the neck, armpits and groin, continuous tiredness, severe weight loss, a continuous dry cough, diarrhoea, THRUSH, unexplained bleeding, shortness of breath, cold sores (HERPES), and fever. People with these types of symptoms are said to have ARC (AIDS-related complex). A number of people with HIV will go on to develop AIDS, which is characterized by several very serious illnesses, any of which may be fatal.

A test can be done on a sample of blood to discover if the HIV infection is present. A positive result means that the virus is present and such people are said to be 'HIV-positive'. A negative result means HIV has not been detected, although it may appear in later tests because the virus can take several months to manifest itself. This test should be done at a SPECIAL CLINIC which deals with SEXUALLY TRANSMITTED DISEASES.

HIV is a very delicate virus which can't live for long periods outside the body. You can't catch it like the flu or common cold virus merely by being near someone who's ill. You also can't get it by touching, shaking hands, sharing the same musical instrument, cooking utensils, telephone or launderette, from swimming in the same pool, or by sharing the toilet or canteen facilities with someone who is HIV-positive. HIV has to pass directly from a body fluid which carries the infection into the bloodstream of another person. These body fluids are blood, URINE, MENSTRUAL blood, SEMEN, FAECES, secretions from the VAGINA, breast milk and saliva.

The most direct way for the virus to be passed on is if someone who injects themselves with drugs uses the same unsterilized needle and syringe as someone who already has the infection. The babies of mothers with HIV may be born with the virus and there is also a possibility of a baby becoming infected with HIV due to breast-feeding. The most common way for the virus to be spread is by

SEXUAL INTERCOURSE (anal or vaginal), when it can be absorbed through the walls of the vagina, the ANUS, and the tip of the PENIS. Deep kissing (see FRENCH) is not considered risky because HIV is not present in large enough quantities in saliva, but ORAL SEX may present a risk – especially CUNNILINGUS during a woman's period. Any sores, cuts or tears on the body, inside the mouth, vagina or anus create a greater chance of infection if either partner is HIV-positive.

The onset of AIDS can be delayed and the symptoms of HIV can be controlled by medicines, diet and general body-care. HIV can stay in the bloodstream for years without any signs of illness. However, someone who is HIV-positive can still pass the infection to someone else, despite the absence of symptoms. Because HIV is so widespread amongst both HETEROSEXUALS and HOMOSEXUALS, everyone who has a sex life or is beginning to have a sex life should take precautions against contracting or passing on this disease by practising SAFER SEX.

homophobia

The 'homo' part of this word is Greek for 'same' and in this context refers to HOMOSEXUALITY. A 'phobia', from the Greek word for 'flight, terror, panic', is an abnormal, irrational fear or hatred of something. Homophobia, the irrational fear or hatred of homosexuality, is still widespread throughout the world.

Homosexuality between consenting adult males may now be legal in most English-speaking countries but there are still laws which discriminate against GAYS. Any form of discrimination tends to increase the amount of ignorance and intolerance that exists among HETEROSEXUALS which only leads to more fear and hatred. Homosexuals are subjected to a great deal of discrimination, making it difficult for them to openly express their feelings of love for each other.

The most extreme form of homophobia is what's known as 'QUEER-bashing'. This occurs when one or more heterosexual man beats up a homosexual simply because he is gay. Other people express their hatred by refusing to give certain jobs to gays or by spreading the fear that a gay man will try to corrupt or sexually ABUSE children. They fail to see that by far the greatest number of people who abuse the young are heterosexual men (see PAEDOPHILE) whose victims are mostly girls. Another argument used by homophobes is that unless homosexuality is stamped out the birth rate will decline to zero. But homosexuality is not a disease that spreads from one person to another and homosexuals aren't people committed to making everyone else gay. The use of words like 'queer', 'poof', or 'FAGGOT' may be only a mild form of homophobia, but they all add to an atmosphere of intolerance.

Sex researchers believe that at least ten per cent of us are homosexual and another forty per cent of us are BISEXUALS who will experience gay or LESBIAN feelings or at least one gay relationship in adult life. It may be that what homophobes really fear is their own deep-seated homosexual feelings. The society we live in appears to teach that to be homosexual is wrong or sick, but ignores the irrationality of homophobia, which is probably more rampant than homosexuality itself.

homosexual (hom-oh-seks-u-al)

Coined (see Glossary) in the 1850s by K. M. Benkert, a doctor from Leipzig in Germany, this comes from the Greek *homos* meaning 'same' and not, as many people mistakenly believe, from the Latin word *homo* meaning 'man'. Homosexuality then, means a female or a male who is sexually attracted to someone of the same sex. The term GAY is now widely used for homosexuality although many female homosexuals prefer LESBIAN.

It's thought that about ten per cent of us are homosexual. No one really knows what makes someone gay and it's probably a combination of different factors. It may be that some people are born gay, connected to the sort of GENES they inherit from their parents. Sigmund Freud, the founder of psychoanalysis, saw homosexuality as a type of NARCISSISM, with the person loved being similar to the person doing the loving. It may also be connected with how a child is brought up – homosexuality may have less to do with a positive urge towards the same sex and more to do with having a fear of the opposite sex.

The safest thing that can be said is that each and every homosexual is different and it's impossible to lump them all together to find a common factor. Some people think you can tell who's gay or lesbian by the way they dress, talk or behave (see CAMP). Because homosexuals have been cruelly persecuted for so long, more gays are attracted to certain jobs or careers (in the theatre, for example) where their STRAIGHT colleagues are more tolerant. But in reality there's no way of telling who is gay and who is not just by looking at them.

When we reach PUBERTY in our early teens, a homosexual phase is so common (see CRUSH) that it's considered a normal part of development. People who hate or fear homosexuality (see HOMO-PHOBIA) don't think of it as 'normal'. It may be less common than heterosexuality but for a gay or a lesbian it is a totally normal way of life (see CLOSET).

Treating someone differently just because they don't conform to the majority is a form of discrimination. You can tell from many of the slang terms that homosexuals have been and are still subjected to a lot of intolerant discrimination and hatred. When used by heterosexuals these words are usually abusive but not if they're used by lesbians and gay men themselves.

Adjectives used for homosexuals of both sexes include BENT, FAG, faggoty, faggy, fairy, fay, flaming, flitty, fruity, homo, KINKY, lacy, light-footed, limp-wristed, mary, nancy, pansy, pink, QUEER, swish.

Slang terms for lesbians include boondagger, bull, bulldagger, bulldyke, BUTCH, diesel-dyke, fairy lady, FEM, FEMME, lesbo, lez, lezzie, man, mary.

Slang terms for gay men include battyboy, capon (a CASTRATED cockerel), daisy, dilly dude, fag, faggot, fairy, flamer, flaming asshole, flaming fruitbar, flit, flower, flute, freak, fruit, fruitcake (from the phrase 'nutty as a fruitcake', implying that gays are crazy), girl, home-boy (a male who can't tear himself away from his mother's apron strings), jackie, limp-wrist, mary, nancy, nancy boy, nell, pansy, poof, poofter, poove, punk, QUEEN, queer, sissy, and swish.

hooker

This American slang word for a PROSTITUTE was first used in the nineteenth century. It may come from the sixteenth-century word *huckster* meaning 'pedlar, hawker, mercenary person'. Another theory suggests 'hooker' was the name given to the female camp-followers of General Joseph Hooker during the American Civil War in the 1860s. Or it may come from a district in New York called Corleon's Hook where prostitutes used to work (see RED LIGHT). The most likely explanation is the verb 'to hook' in the sense of trapping or snaring someone into doing something improper, undesirable or foolish. Some men would use this argument to justify their actions, despite the fact that it's their choice and decision to pay a woman for sex.

hormones

These are chemical substances released into the bloodstream by organs known as glands in order to regulate the function of other organs. When we reach PUBERTY our bodies start to produce sex hormones which make us mature physically. These are produced mainly in the GONADS – the OVARIES in females and the TESTES in males. There are three groups of sex hormones: androgens, OESTROGENS, and PROGESTOGENS. Both sexes have all three, but the proportions differ.

The oestrogen and progestogen hormones in a female influence the development of her secondary sex characteristics – the rounded shape she grows into as a woman, her breasts, her underarm and PUBIC HAIR, and the shape and colour of her VULVA. PROGESTERONE, one of the progestogen group of hormones, is produced in the CORPUS LUTEUM and is mostly concerned with the preparation and maintenance of pregnancy.

Androgens predominate in boys, the most powerful being testosterone which is produced in the TESTICLES and controls male secondary sex characteristics such as the breaking of his voice when it goes deeper, facial and bodily hair, a more muscular physique, and the development of his PENIS and testicles.

hustler

This is another term for a PROSTITUTE dating from the 1950s. It's probably connected to the use of 'hustle' meaning 'to beg, steal' and it may well have started as Black American slang. One of the first people to use it was the jazz trumpeter Louis Armstrong in his autobiography *Satchmo, My Life in New Orleans* (1954).

hymen

From the Greek word meaning 'membrane', the hymen is a very thin layer of skin tissue that partly covers the entrance to the VAGINA.

Not all girls are born with one and most hymens have one or more holes in them which allows menstrual blood to flow out of the vagina when she has her PERIOD. Many hymens get stretched and wither away if a young girl does a lot of fairly active exercise, uses a TAMPON or MASTURBATES. Having a hymen is not necessarily a sign of VIRGINITY. In societies that still believe it is, a new bride is often given a small blood-soaked sponge to push up her vagina so that blood spills on to the sheets to 'prove' she's a virgin.

It's widely thought that when a hymen is broken it is incredibly painful and bloody. This may be true for a very small percentage of girls whose hymen is thicker than average. But the majority, if they feel anything, experience very little bleeding and perhaps a short, sharp pain. It may well be that any pain a girl or woman feels the first time she has SEXUAL INTERCOURSE is the result of her own fear and perhaps her partner's inexperience (see FOREPLAY).

MAIDENHEAD and CHERRY, the two most widely-used slang terms for the hymen are also used to mean virginity. The rather violent-sounding term 'cherry-splitter' was a popular term for the penis in the nineteenth century.

I

illegitimate (ill-ee-*jit*-im-it)
Someone who is illegitimate was born to parents who were not married at the time. See also BASTARD.

immoral
If you describe someone as immoral, it means you don't think their behaviour conforms with generally accepted standards of what is morally right. Sexual morals refer to how people treat their sexual partner. Someone who is not honest or fair is immoral (see ABUSE). Immorality depends a lot on the individual and on the sort of society they come from. Some people think PROMISCUITY is immoral, while others think that having more than one sexual partner is acceptable as long as everyone is honest with each other about what is happening.

importune See SOLICIT.

impotence
'Im' before a word often means 'not' (as in 'imbalance' and 'imperfect'); 'potent' comes from the Latin for 'to be powerful' and 'to be able' which is related to the Gothic word for 'bridegroom', the Greek for 'husband' and the Sanskrit word for 'master'. Most regular dictionaries define impotence as a male's incapacity to perform SEXUAL INTER-COURSE due to an inability to get or maintain an ERECTION, and as a male who is STERILE. Medical dictionaries give a wider definition which includes women. A girl or woman who is unable to have intercourse either because of a malformed vagina (which is very rare) or because of painful inflammation which causes the muscles around the vagina to contract, is also described as impotent. This is popularly

(but incorrectly) called FRIGIDITY. (See also DYSPAREUNIA and VAGINISMUS.)

For both sexes impotence usually has psychological causes. When a boy or man is unable to get or maintain an erection his partner often thinks that it's because he doesn't fancy her but the reason is more likely to be a lack of confidence in himself. Feeling anxious about sex, especially the first time when everyone is bound to be a bit nervous (see VIRGINITY), often leads to PREMATURE EJACULATION. Feeling scared that his partner might fall pregnant, give him a SEXUALLY TRANSMITTED DISEASE, or that his parents or another partner will find out he's having sex, can also make a boy impotent. The pressure on a male to perform well is a very common cause of impotence.

Most males suffer from short-term impotence at some time during their life. It often happens when they're feeling a bit depressed and not being able to get an erection makes them feel even more depressed. Most couples find that patience, love and understanding make the impotence go away. If it persists, a doctor or a specially-trained sex therapist may be able to sort out the problem (see COUNSELLING).

in flagrante delicto (in flag-*gran*-tay day-*lik*-toh)
This Latin phrase, literally 'in blazing crime', means being caught in the very act of having SEXUAL INTERCOURSE, especially with someone you're not supposed to be having sex with. (See ADULTERY, PREMARITAL SEX.)

in vitro fertilization See FERTILIZATION.

incest
From the Latin word meaning 'impure', a sexual relationship between close relatives is known as incest. Thousands of years ago before inter-tribal contacts began to develop, some incest or inbreeding was inevitable among early humankind. But even in ancient times it's thought there was probably some sort of unspoken law, or TABOO, against SEXUAL INTERCOURSE between very close blood relatives such

as daughters, sons, mothers and fathers. Societies that persistently inbreed produce people who have very similar genes and this makes them unable to adapt to changing conditions or new diseases.

In ancient Egyptian and Greek mythology there are countless examples of gods and mortals who had sex with their close blood relatives, but the people themselves lived according to certain laws which made incest unacceptable. The Book of Leviticus in the Old Testament spells out the Judaeo-Christian definition of incest:

None of you shall approach any one near of kin to him to uncover naked-ness.

It then gives a long list of relatives who must not marry or have sexual relations with each other. These include fathers, mothers, sisters, brothers, grandparents and great grandparents, aunts, uncles, step-parents, step-sisters and brothers, daughters and sons-in-law. Sex with your sister's husband or your brother's wife was only allowed if your sister or brother was dead.

Laws against incest may have originated from society's fear of extinction due to inbreeding but today they exist to provide the basis of protecting young people from sexual ABUSE by someone in the position of parent or guardian. Legal definitions vary from country to country and, in the USA, from state to state. Nieces and nephews are covered in some places, and in others the list of taboo relationships has been reduced, as in Scotland where a step-child may marry its step-parent once they are over the age of twenty-one. As attitudes change, alterations to the list of outlawed incestuous relationships are suggested – some people, for example, believe that consenting sisters and brothers over the age of eighteen should be allowed to have sexual relationships.

Incest and abuse of care is more widespread than many people want to believe. It happens in every kind of family – rich and poor, upper-class, middle-class and working-class, blue-collar and white-collar, black, Asian and white peoples and among people from every religion. The most common form of incest takes place between girls and their fathers or step-fathers. It happens at any age. It may be just one incident or it may go on for years.

It is very difficult for a child to prevent itself from being sexually abused, especially by a parent or someone who is loved and trusted. Some victims of incest feel guilty for years after either because they felt some sexual pleasure at the time or because they were encouraged to take an active part. Most of us find that when we are touched or stroked, especially by someone we love, our bodies react with pleasure in a way that is beyond our control.

However it happened or whatever actually took place, it is *always* the older person who is responsible for committing the crime. Because it is such a shocking crime to most people, many children or young people who report it find that no one believes them. If it happens to you and you can find someone you trust to talk to about it, you will feel much better than if you bottle it all up. There are several national helplines and organizations that will give you confidential advice and support (see COUNSELLING).

indecency

An indecent act is any action with a sexual element which outrages public opinion. 'Indecent exposure' is a formal term for flashing or EXHIBITIONISM, which is when a person gets sexual pleasure from intentionally exposing his or her GENITALS. 'Indecent assault' is a British legal term for a physical touching which falls short of RAPE. Legal definitions differ. For example, in New York State, the violent forcing of a knife or bottle into a woman's vagina is treated as rape but elsewhere it falls into the category of indecent assault.

On a less violent level, deciding what is decent and what is indecent varies in different societies and also changes over time. In Victorian society, for instance, it was thought to be indecent for a woman to show her ankle in public and the sight of her knee was definitely out of bounds. In some strict Muslim societies women are expected to keep completely covered up in public. The law, which takes a bit of time to catch up with public opinion on this matter, sometimes produces some absurd situations. Until the 1960s, in the UK it was legally acceptable for a stripper to appear naked but it was criminally 'indecent' if she moved even a little finger.

infertility

The word 'fertile' comes from the Latin for 'to carry or to bear'. Although it's obviously women who actually bear or carry children in their wombs, 'infertile' is used to describe both women and men who are unable to have children.

There can be several reasons for a woman's infertility. She may fail to OVULATE, her FALLOPIAN TUBES may be blocked, or a fertilized EGG may not become properly attached to the lining of the WOMB, in which case she will have a MISCARRIAGE, or spontaneous ABORTION. For some women infertility can be due to emotional reasons or ill health.

In males, the cause may be that their SPERM are STERILE, that the number of sperm in their SEMEN is abnormally low, or their sperm may be exceptionally dozy and fail to swim from the VAGINA to the Fallopian tubes where fertilization takes place.

Anyone who finds it difficult to conceive should consult a doctor who may be able to suggest HORMONE treatment or *in vitro* fertilization (see FERTILIZATION).

infibulation See CLITORIDECTOMY.

insemination

From the Latin for 'to put seed into', this is the act of introducing SEMEN into the female reproductive organs (see SEXUAL INTERCOURSE).

intercourse See SEXUAL INTERCOURSE.

Intrauterine Device (IUD)

Also called a coil or loop, the intrauterine device involves putting something inside the UTERUS, or WOMB, to prevent PREGNANCY. It works by causing changes to the womb-lining which prevent a FERTILIZED OVUM from becoming attached to it. They must be inserted by a medically-trained person.

IUDs come in several different shapes, are made of metal or plastic, and have a couple of tiny threads attached to the end. They are flexible enough to be pressed into a narrow tube-like syringe which is inserted through the CERVIX into the womb. When they are pushed out of this tube they spring back into shape and the threads hang down through the cervix into the very top of the vagina where they can be felt to check if the IUD is in position. This should be done at least once a week.

As a means of BIRTH CONTROL they are very effective – out of every hundred girls and women fitted with an IUD only two will fall pregnant each year. But many doctors don't like giving them to young women or women who haven't had a baby because they can have serious side effects such as infections in the internal sex organs and, very occasionally, perforation of the walls of the womb, which can threaten a woman's fertility. Some girls and women find that their PERIOD becomes unacceptably heavy and painful. Because of their history of causing complications and the legal actions that followed, the manufacture of IUDs has virtually ceased in the USA. (This hasn't prevented some unscrupulous firms from off-loading them on to women in undeveloped countries.)

As a means of preventing the spread of SEXUALLY TRANSMITTED DISEASES such as HIV, the virus that can lead to AIDS, they are completely ineffective. (See SAFER SEX.)

IVF (*in vitro* fertilization) See FERTILIZATION.

J

jack off

In the USA, 'to jack off' is a widely-used slang term for MASTURBA-
TION (usually male masturbation). PORNOGRAPHIC magazines are
sometimes called 'Jack journals' because many men masturbate over
the photos of naked women in them.

'Jack' in this sense may have been shortened from EJACULATION,
or it may come from the affectionate use of 'Jack' as a nickname for
the PENIS, especially with an ERECTION. Or it may have been used as
a slightly more polite version of 'jerk off' which has been considered
a vulgar term for masturbation since the eighteenth century. Both
'jack' and 'jerk' are slang for a weak-minded person; this may be
because of the myth that too much masturbation makes you stupid.

Various different senses of Jack over the years may explain why it
became a name for the penis. Although they're not used much these
days, Jack and Jill have been terms for male and female sweethearts
since the fifteenth century. Jack is also the Knave in playing cards,
traditionally a male soldier or servant ranking below the Queen.
Since servants were well-known for their unprincipled PROMISCUOUS
behaviour, any rogue came to be referred to as 'a Jack'. A Jack-in-
the-box, for example, is the name given to a children's toy which has
a small male doll inside that springs out to surprise anyone who
opens the box. 'Jack-in-the-box' has also been slang for the penis, an
unborn child in the womb, and as rhyming slang for 'POX', a popular
term for SYPHILIS. By the nineteenth century, Jack was used for any
man or fellow whose name wasn't known.

As a verb, 'to jack' became a slang term for SEXUAL INTERCOURSE,
and 'to jack it' meant to have an ORGASM. To boys and men who
thought of their penis or an erection in terms of a friendly but
naughty companion in need of a name, Jack was an obvious choice.

Other male names used for the penis include DICK, Percy, JOHN, Johnny, John Thomas and Willy.

jailbait

Jailbait (or gaolbait), johnnybait, and bedbait are all slang terms for a sexually attractive girl under the AGE OF CONSENT. Any boy or man who has sex with a girl under this age is technically guilty of RAPE, INDECENT assault or statutory rape and, depending on his age, may be punished by being sent to prison.

The word 'bait' comes from an Old Norse verb meaning 'to hunt' and the suggestion behind the word 'jailbait' is that the girl is luring a man to tempt him to break the law. (See also LOLITA, NYMPHET.)

Jane

In the UK, Jane is simply a popular female first name (since the fourteenth century from the French *Jehanne*, from the male name *Jean*). In the past, however, a 'Jane Shore' was rhyming slang (see Glossary) for a WHORE from the name of the mistress of King Edward IV, who was the subject of a play by Nicholas Rowe (1674–1718). See also LOTHARIO. 'Jane' or 'Lady Jane' has also been slang for VAGINA – it is used affectionately in this sense by the two central lovers in D. H. Lawrence's famous novel LADY CHATTERLEY'S LOVER.

In Australia and the USA 'Jane' has been slang for a woman, for 'vagina' (or CUNT'), for a woman's public toilet, and for a PROSTITUTE. In America, 'Jane Doe' is the female equivalent of 'John Doe'. Similarly, 'John' is slang for a male, a toilet, and for the male client of a female prostitute.

Along with 'dame' and 'doll', 'Jane' was one of the most popular terms for a female (usually an attractive or apparently sexually-available woman) in the USA in the 1950s and 1960s. Over the centuries other female names (Molly, Nancy, Jessie, Jemmy, Sheila etc) have become slang and/or negative terms for a female, a female sweetheart, female genitalia, a female prostitute and, sometimes, for an effeminate man. The women's movement and changes of fashion in slang terms have made 'Jane' less popular than it used to be (see OBSOLESCENT in the Glossary).

jerk See JACK OFF.

Jezebel

A Jezebel or a painted Jezebel is a HARLOT, or a woman who flaunts herself by wearing make-up and showy clothes in order to attract a man. The term comes from the Book of Kings in the Old Testament:

When Jehu came to Jezreel, Jezebel heard of it; and she painted her eyes, and adorned her head and looked out of the window.

For the double crime of being the wife of Jehu's enemy and for looking at another man, Jezebel was thrown out of the window 'and some of her blood spattered on the wall and on the horses, and they trampled on her'. See also SCARLET WOMAN.

jism

This is mainly American slang for SEMEN. It's also used for any liquid that is slimy and nasty. In another sense it means power and impact, rather like spunk (also slang for semen), which can mean courage and guts.

jock rot

Jock rot or jock itch is what many North Americans call a type of ringworm of the crotch caused by a fungus. The medical name is *Tinea Cruris*. It's sometimes also called 'dhobie itch'. Dhobie (or dhobi) is the Hindi word for 'washerman', and ringworm got this name from the (false) belief that the disease was caught from newly-washed clothes. The symptoms are an itching and a sore, reddish, damp feeling on and around the SCROTUM.

Many men with jock rot wrongly believe that they've got some serious SEXUALLY TRANSMITTED DISEASE. It's actually a type of athlete's foot infection of the pubic region and is usually caused by wearing clothes that are too tight or that make you sweat, and by not drying yourself carefully. A light rubbing of cornstarch may cure it, but if it doesn't go away a doctor may have to prescribe a stronger fungicide.

'Jock' is slang for 'athlete', shortened from the jockstrap male athletes wear to protect their GENITALS. Jockstrap got its name from the eighteenth-century use of the word 'jock' meaning the genitals of both females and males. It later came to refer only to the PENIS and TESTICLES. 'To jock' was nineteenth-century slang for SEXUAL INTERCOURSE, from 'jockum' meaning penis. 'Jockum-cloy' is an obsolete (see Glossary) term meaning 'sexual intercourse with a woman' which borrowed the word 'cloy' meaning 'to steal' from thieves' jargon (see Glossary). A chamber pot was sometimes called a 'jockum-gage' making a pun on the word 'gage' in the sense of something deposited as a pledge of performance (gage comes from an old Gothic word meaning pledge from which we also get the word wage). A 'jockum-gagger' was a man who lived on his wife's earnings as a PROSTITUTE (see PIMP).

John

In the past, a John and a Johnny (or Johnnie) have been affectionate terms for a fellow or a chap – what today might be called 'a regular guy' – and for a male sweetheart (see also JACK OFF). In the 1950s 'a John' was American slang for a man who paid for a woman's rent and expenses in return for sex. It later came to be used in the world of PROSTITUTION as slang for a male customer as well as, more widely, for a woman's steady date. Male HOMOSEXUALS borrowed the word to refer to a wealthy, elderly GAY man who kept a younger man in a sexual relationship (see SUGAR DADDY).

Although it took three centuries, the development in meaning from a male lover to a PENIS was an obvious one. By the nineteenth century the penis was sometimes given the nicknames of John Thomas, Johnny and, in the twentieth century, Johnson. The same thing happened to other male names such as Jack and DICK, all suggesting a friendly relationship between a man and his sex organ. In the twentieth century a Johnny bag, later shortened to Johnny, became slang for a CONDOM.

K

Kama Sutra (karma sootra)

This is the name of one of the oldest and most famous Indian sex manuals. It is thought to have been compiled by a Hindu wise man who belonged to the Vatsyayana sect of Hinduism some time between the third and fifth centuries before Christ was born. 'Kama' (or karma) is the Sanskrit word (see Glossary) for pleasure and love, and 'sutra' originally meant a thread or a string of rules to live by. The *Kama Sutra* is a classic work of erotic literature, perhaps the first in which love figured strongly in a book about sexual knowhow.

Vatsyayana (as the author is known) listed seven different types of 'congress' or SEXUAL INTERCOURSE, from 'loving congress' between true lovers to the sexual relationship between a gentleman and a low-caste servant for the purpose of relieving the man's sexual needs. He also listed forty different, highly acrobatic, positions for sexual intercourse. As well as classifying and giving detailed descriptions about how to have sex the book recognized four types of love: the simple love of sexual intercourse which is described as being like a drug habit; love-addiction to aspects of sex such as kissing or embracing; love consisting of the mutual attraction between two people; and a one-sided kind of love that springs from the admiration of a lover's beauty.

Some of the advice offered in the book isn't what you'd find in many sex manuals today:

'Blows with the fist should be given on the back of the woman while she is sitting on the lap of the man . . .'

And it's definitely written from a male point of view:

'When a man is endeavouring to seduce one woman, he should not attempt to seduce any other at the same time. But after he has succeeded with the

110

first … he can keep her affections by giving her presents that she likes, and then commence making up to another woman.'

But it has a strong sense of the need for shared pleasure:

'An ingenious person should multiply the kinds of congress after the fashion of the different kinds of beasts and birds. For these different kinds of congress, performed according to the usage of each country and the liking of each individual, generate love, friendship, and respect in the hearts of women.'

The *Kama Sutra* was published in English in 1883 under the direction of Sir Richard Burton, an English literary gentleman who translated several exotic erotic works such as the *Arabian Nights* and THE PERFUMED GARDEN.

Kaposi's sarcoma (KS) (kap-*poh*-zees *sar*-ko-mah)

Sarcoma is the medical term for a cancerous tumour. Kaposi's sarcoma is a CANCER-like disease of the skin named after an Austrian skin specialist, B. K. Kaposi. It was first identified in the 1800s and occurred mainly in elderly Italian or Ashkenazi Jewish men. It is now very common among people with AIDS and is one of the main causes of their deaths.

In its very early stages KS appears as a small pink or purplish patch on the skin which often has a bruise-like, brownish-yellow stain around the new patches. These painless cancerous patches eventually increase in size, appear elsewhere on the skin surface, and spread to internal organs.

There is no cure for KS, but radiotherapy may be used to get rid of or reduce the KS patches if they appear on the face, and some drugs can slow down the spread of the disease.

kerb crawler

This British term refers to a man who slowly drives his car close to the edge of a pavement with the aim of looking to pick up a PROSTITUTE or to entice or force a woman into his car in order to have sex with him. Kerb crawling is a crime and can be a form of sexual HARASSMENT to girls and women who are not prostitutes but just happen to be walking down a street.

kinky

Kinky means 'twisted, curled' and is used informally to mean having sexual tastes or habits which most other people think are a bit unusual or peculiar. Anything more extreme is usually referred to as deviant behaviour (see PERVERSION).

kiss

Kisses can be polite or passionate, simple or sexy. Our lips are one of the most sensitive areas of our bodies (see EROGENOUS ZONE), but there's all the difference in the world between kissing an aunt goodbye and giving someone you love or really fancy the sort of kiss that turns you both on (see AROUSAL).

FRENCH kissing, (also known as deep or soul kissing), when we push our tongue into our partner's mouth can be especially EROTIC. In many cultures kissing is an important part of FOREPLAY. But kissing is not universal and is not generally practised by the Ainu, Okinawans, Andamanese, Vietnamese, Somali, Lepcha, Cewa or Sirinoco peoples.

knock

In the sense of a firm blow on something solid like a door, the word knock is known as an onomatopoeia (see Glossary). But it was the action rather than the sound that produced the verb 'to knock' as a slang term for SEXUAL INTERCOURSE in the sixteenth century. This led to 'knock' being used for the PENIS two hundred years later. 'Knock off' is probably more common now than plain 'knock' but it has a hint of disapproval plus a suggestion of very quick or emotionally uninvolved sex about it, e.g. 'He knocked off his best friend's girl-friend'.

A woman's breasts may be called 'knockers'. Once she has been 'knocked off', she may find herself 'knocked up', which has been a popular slang for PREGNANCY since the nineteenth century.

L

labia (labb-ee-ah)

This is the Latin for 'lips'. Lip comes from the Greek word meaning 'fatty tissue'. The outer fatty folds of skin around the vulva are called the *labia majora* which translates literally as 'larger lips'; the inner folds closest to the VAGINA are the *labia minora* meaning 'smaller lips'.

The outer lips normally lie close together in order to protect a woman's genitals. If they are spread open, or if she is sexually aroused when they open naturally by themselves, the sensitive inner lips can be seen, although sometimes they poke out naturally beyond the outer lips. Where the inner lips come together at the front they form a small hood over the CLITORIS called the PREPUCE.

Lady Chatterley's Lover

Since this novel by the English novelist D. H. Lawrence was published in the late 1920s, it has been regarded as a major literary classic by some and as one of the dirtiest books around by others. Because of his detailed and, some would say, poetic descriptions of sex and his use of FOUR-LETTER WORDS, Lawrence had to have it printed privately in Italy. It wasn't published in its full uncensored version until 1960, when Penguin Books bravely published the full text. They were promptly prosecuted for obscenity.

The long legal battle over this book had more highlights than most soap operas. Many well-known literary figures sprang to its defence and newspaper journalists went through agonies as they tried to find publishable words (see EUPHEMISM in the Glossary) to tell their readers what had been said in court. In a shocked voice the prosecuting lawyer listed the so-called OBSCENE words:

'The word "FUCK" or "fucking" occurs no less than thirty times. I have added them all up. "CUNT" fourteen times; "BALLS" thirteen times; "SHIT" and "ARSE" six times apiece; 'COCK four times; "PISS" three times . . .'

Seemingly unaware of the lives of ordinary women and men, he asked the jury whether it was the sort of book that one's wife or servant should be allowed to read. The reference in the novel to ANAL INTERCOURSE was not mentioned in court – the ADULTERY, ILLEGITIMACY, and the notion of an upper-class lady falling in love with a servant was quite enough to upset the feelings of those who wanted it banned.

The prosecution lost its case and some people claim that the uncensored publication of this novel ushered in the decade which became known as the age of PERMISSIVENESS. Those opposed to its publication probably saw the 1960s more as an age of PROMISCUITY.

lascivious

From the Latin for 'sportive, LUSTFUL, WANTON', this describes someone who shows an excessive interest in or DESIRE for sex.

lay

'To lie with' meaning 'to have SEXUAL INTERCOURSE with' is found in early English translations of the Bible, but it's possible that the modern slang use of the term came from the literal sense of 'laying' a woman down on her back for sexual purposes (see MISSIONARY POSITION). In the mid-nineteenth century, 'lay' came to be used among criminals as a slang term for an expedition of thieves for a criminal purpose, for a site of a robbery or a robbery itself, and for a person or place that was robbed. In the twentieth century 'a lay' became slang for a woman thought of as a SEX OBJECT and as a term for sexual intercourse from the male point of view. Since the 1960s women have used it in the same way.

lechery

Lechery means an excessive or gluttonous indulgence in sexual activity; a lecher is a man who virtually does nothing other than think about, have, or want to have sex (today he would probably be called 'a dirty old man' – whatever his actual age). If this paints a picture of a man drooling and licking his lips it's not surprising, since the word originates from an Old French word meaning 'to lick'. 'Lechery' later came to mean 'living in DEBAUCHERY'. Lickerish, also spelled liquorish (no connection with alcohol), is an obsolete (see Glossary) word which once meant 'fond of good food, greedy, lecherous'.

lesbian

This word for a female HOMOSEXUAL comes from the Greek island of Lesbos where the poet SAPPHO lived in 600 BC. From the remaining fragments of her poetry it is believed that Sappho loved women rather than men:

> Beautiful women,
> my feelings for you
> will never falter.

'Lesbian' wasn't coined (see Glossary) until the 1890s. In the early seventeenth century *fricatrice* and *tribade* from the Latin and Greek verbs meaning 'to rub' were used.

Sexually, lesbians do what most HETEROSEXUALS do. They can make each other COME by rubbing their partner's CLITORIS and some may use a DILDO either to play with on their clitoris or to put into the vagina. You can't tell just by looking at someone if they're gay or straight. The notion of a masculine-looking, BUTCH woman with big boots, hairy legs, and a cropped hairstyle is a stereotype and no stereotype paints a true picture. Some lesbians do dress in a butch style because they have COME OUT and want to publicly identify themselves as women who love women, but this tells you only about the style of clothes they wear rather than any biological difference from STRAIGHT women.

Unlike male homosexuality, lesbianism has never been illegal. It's said that when Queen Victoria's ministers were drafting a bill to outlaw homosexuality they dropped the clause referring to lesbianism in embarrassment because she refused to believe that it existed. But this doesn't mean that lesbians haven't been or aren't discriminated against. When British author Radclyffe Hall wrote *The Well of Loneliness* in 1928 it was banned for ten years because of the lesbian relationship she wrote about – despite protests from respected literary figures like George Bernard Shaw and A. E. Housman. And although lesbianism isn't illegal, women working in sensitive government departments still have to sign a form saying that they're not lesbian (if they admitted it they'd probably be sacked).

HOMOPHOBIA, the fear and hatred of homosexuals of both GENDERS, expresses itself in many ways – few, if any, of the slang terms for a lesbian are ones which lesbians themselves choose, such as Amy-John, boondagger, bull, bulldagger, bulldyke, butch, diesel-dyke, fairy lady, FEM, FEMME, lesbo, lez, lezzie, man, Mary, top sergeant. (See also GAY, QUEER.)

leukorrhoea/leucorrhoea (luke-o-*ree*-ah)

Leukos is the Greek word for white. Leukorrhoea, literally 'flow of white', is a thickish, sticky white discharge from the WOMB or VAGINA consisting of mucus and discarded cells. It can be an early sign of pregnancy. Any girl or woman who gets this (or any other) discharge should go to her doctor or to a SPECIAL CLINIC which deals with SEXUALLY TRANSMITTED DISEASES and other genital infections which aren't necessarily caused by sex.

lewd (rhymes with rude)

This word is becoming obsolete (see Glossary) in modern language. It generally refers to someone who is unprincipled, and whose actions are not morally acceptable within the boundaries of Christian behaviour. Other terms for it are unlearned, low, vulgar, ignorant, ill-conditioned, LASCIVIOUS, unchaste (see CHASTITY) and finally, 'sexually coarse and crude'.

libido

The Latin word *libido* meaning 'wish, desire' and 'LUST' comes from another word meaning 'to please' which is the root of the word love.

Libido is used by psychoanalysts to refer to an emotional or mental energy that comes from biological sexual instincts. According to Sigmund Freud, the founder of psychoanalysis who, at the end of the nineteenth century first used the word, our libido is connected to love in the same way that hunger is connected to the instinct to eat. In general use libido is used more simply to mean sexual desire.

licentious

This is a formal term for someone who behaves in a sexually IMMORAL way. It comes from a Latin word meaning 'capricious', which means to change your mind or behaviour frequently and unexpectedly. This means that the character LADY CHATTERLEY in the novel by D.H. Lawrence can't be described as licentious, nor can Fanny Hill in the novel by John Cleland – they may have had affairs but they stuck to their own moral code. DON JUAN, however, could be described as licentious since he seduced women by giving the impression that he loved them and then cruelly discarded them on a whim.

lingam

In the ancient Hindi language of Sanskrit (see Glossary), lingam literally means 'characteristic'. It came to be used for PENIS-shaped symbols made of stone which represent the god Shiva. These symbols, worshipped by the Hindus, symbolize Shiva's reproductive powers, believed to act as a charm against STERILITY. The female counterpart of the lingam is the YONI.

Lolita

In 1955 the Russian-born American writer Vladimir Nabokov wrote a novel called *Lolita*, which is widely regarded as a literary classic. It's about a middle-aged man named Humbert Humbert who sexually desires a young girl to such an extent that he marries the mother in order to seduce her. He describes Lolita as a NYMPHET. Only after he has abducted Lolita and has sex with her does Humbert Humbert come to any awareness of the physical and mental pain he caused his step-daughter.

The words 'Lolita' and 'nymphet' are used to describe a sexually precocious girl (under the AGE OF CONSENT) who seduces older men. This is the classic viewpoint of many men who sexually abuse young girls – putting the blame on them and refusing to admit to any responsibility or guilt. (See CHILD SEXUAL ABUSE, INCEST.)

loose

When this word first entered the English language in the fourteenth century it meant 'free from bonds or from any physical restraint'. It may come from an older word which first meant 'lying, deceit' and then 'something that is frivolous, lax'. Within a hundred years 'loose' also meant 'naked and free from moral restraint'. By the fifteenth century, it was used of both women and men who were sexually PROMISCUOUS. To describe a man as loose meant he was thought to be a bit of a rascal, while to call a woman loose meant she was a PROSTITUTE (see DOUBLE STANDARD). Today 'loose' is mostly used to describe a girl or woman who sleeps with lots of different partners. A loose woman is sometimes also called a SCARLET WOMAN.

Lothario (loth-ah-ree-o)

In 1703, the English dramatist Nicholas Rowe (1674–1718) wrote a play called *The Fair Penitent* in which a character called Lothario seduces several women. Ever since, the word Lothario has been used, usually in a positive sense, to describe a boy or man who persuades members of the female sex to make love with him by pretending he is emotionally committed to them while all the time he is, in fact, an emotional coward. Other terms used in much the same way include DON JUAN, rake, libertine. See also DOUBLE STANDARD.

love

Poets and novelists seem to find it easier than lexicographers to define love. To anyone who is or has been in love, definitions like 'strong affection', 'emotional attachment', 'devotion and admiration' don't really sum it up. Sexual desire for most people is a very strong part of being in love, which is presumably why the term 'to make love' is used for SEXUAL INTERCOURSE. Many people have sex without being in love. And you can love someone without having sex with them (see PLATONIC).

The English poet Gavin Ewart has perhaps summed up what love is about better than anyone else:

One Word Love Poem

You!

love-bite
This is a British term for a passionate type of KISS which involves biting or sucking your partner – often on the neck. It leaves a blemish or bruise caused by the slight damage to the tiny blood vessels under the skin. In the USA it's called a HICKEY.

lubricant (*loo*-bree-kant)
When a girl or woman is feeling sexually AROUSED, her VAGINA produces a natural secretion which makes her VULVA wet, or lubricated. This makes it easier for the PENIS to enter the vagina and move up and down inside her during SEXUAL INTERCOURSE. (See also ANAL INTERCOURSE.) If there isn't enough lubrication, sex can make the GENITALS of both partners feel a bit sore. Some couples use a bit of spittle or a lubricated CONDOM to help. You can also buy tubes of lubricating jelly ('KY Jelly' is the best-known brand), which is water-based. This is important because an oil-based substance such as petroleum jelly ('Vaseline'), Nivea cream or baby oil can cause holes in a condom. A water-based SPERMICIDE also provides lubrication.

lust
This word is generally used to mean uncontrollable sexual desire, which has nothing to do with love. In the Christian Church lust is one of the seven deadly sins. St Augustine, one of the early Christian philosophers, connected lust and sex with the idea of Original Sin in the garden of Eden. He claimed that when Adam and Eve disobeyed God by eating the forbidden fruit, they became aware of selfish, lustful impulses which they couldn't control. As a result they became

ashamed of their nakedness and sewed fig leaves together to hide their genitals.

In Victorian times the view that sex without lust was better than sex with lust was felt so strongly that some physicians suggested men should have sex with a PROSTITUTE rather than with their wives!

M

machismo (mak-*kiz*-moe)

From the Spanish word for 'male', machismo became part of the English language from Spanish-Mexican, meaning an excessive sense of MASCULINE pride, an exaggerated awareness and assertion of masculinity. Macho is the adjective used to describe a man who exaggerates his virility to the point of boastful aggressiveness.

madam

In medieval times the French term *ma dame* meaning 'my mother' was used by children to address their mother. It seems to have been rather a respectful title because it was also how queens, high-ranking ladies and nuns were addressed. By the sixteenth century it was a title for a married woman; single ones were called MISTRESS. But strangely, two hundred years later a mistress (a woman kept by a man as his lover) was called a madam which also meant a PROSTITUTE. Since Victorian times the term madam has been used for a female owner or manager of a BROTHEL.

maidenhead

When 'maiden' first entered the English language around the year 1000 it meant a girl or a young unmarried woman. A generation later it meant a female VIRGIN. Sometimes it was also used for a man: King Malcolm IV of Scotland (1141–1165), because he was kind, generous and CHASTE, was known as 'Malcolm the Maiden'. By the end of the fourteenth century 'maid' also meant a female domestic servant – usually a young, unmarried one.

Maidenhead has been used since medieval times to mean both virginity and, informally, the HYMEN. In Samuel Johnson's masterly dictionary published in 1755 it's defined as 'newness, freshness, uncontaminated state'. He pointed out that 'this is now becoming a low word', which may have been because maiden had become a slang term for a WHORE.

CHERRY is a widely-used slang term for virginity and the hymen.

make love

When this expression first appeared in the fifteenth century it was thought to be a rather vulgar way of saying 'to court' or 'woo' in the sense of trying to win someone's heart. Over the years it became less vulgar but also a bit more explicit; by the end of the eighteenth century it referred to something as bold as stealing a kiss. In the twentieth century the phrase came to mean 'to have SEXUAL INTERCOURSE'.

The sexual sense of 'to make love' has more or less taken over completely from the earlier senses of wooing and courting, and people are sometimes surprised when they hear some of the songs from the 1940s in which singers warbled romantically about 'making love' – but they were either using the term in its original mild wooing sense or making a slightly naughty *double entendre* (see Glossary) on the two meanings.

The Canadians were the first to shorten the expression 'to make love' to 'to make it'. And 'on the make' was used by American males to mean a sexual conquest. 'Making out' is mostly used by teenagers in North America when they are talking about having sex but don't want to use formal terms such as COPULATION or FUCKING. But 'making out' can also mean *not* going 'ALL THE WAY'; Americans often use it to mean what is more often called necking or SNOGGING in the UK.

male chauvinist pig (*show*-vin-ist)

A chauvinist, from the nineteenth century French patriot named Nicholas Chauvin, is someone who rather belligerently and uncritically loves their country or a cause. A male chauvinist is a male who believes men are superior to women. Many women in the late 1960s began to refer to SEXIST men as 'male chauvinist pigs'.

Pig has been used since the sixteenth century as a term of abuse for someone who is thought to be stubborn, greedy and mean and who loves to live in his or her own dirt. Police have been called pigs since the end of the eighteenth century.

mammogram

This is an X-ray screening test for CANCER of the BREAST which can detect the disease before there are any symptoms, so it may be cured at an early stage.

masculinity (mass-kew-*lin*-itty)

From the Latin word for male, masculinity means 'typical of a male' or 'what it means to be a man'. The problem with defining masculinity is that what it means to be a man is constantly changing and different societies and groups of people have different ideas. To some, a tough, aggressive 'Rambo'-type is thought to be really masculine. But to others this sort of MACHO man is a bit ridiculous. Back in the sixteenth century a 'real' man was expected to know how to fight and control and dominate his wife but he also had to know how to dance, play a musical instrument, read Latin and Greek, and be able to write a love sonnet. This ideal of the Renaissance man, however, only applied to the aristocracy; a male peasant would have had to prove his masculinity in less sophisticated and artistic ways.

But masculinity has almost always involved notions of strength, aggression, lack of emotion and violence towards women. A male who chooses not to fight, who openly expresses his emotions, who gets involved in child care and takes on domestic responsibilities is widely thought to be EFFEMINATE, although even this is changing. During the Gulf War of 1991 the television showed pictures of American and British soldiers who talked about their fear and some were even seen to be crying. Some viewers may have thought they were weak and 'sissy' (from the word sister) and therefore not very masculine while others thought that their honesty made them even more courageous and manly.

When it comes to sex, ideas about masculinity are also changing.

There are still some people (males and females) who think that men who insist on using a CONDOM when they make love are not masculine. Others believe that the fact that more males are showing that they care not just about themselves but also for their partner, is a sign that our ideas about masculinity are changing for the better.

masochism (masso-kism)

The Austrian novelist and dramatist Leopold von Sacher-Masoch (1836–1895) wrote a novel called *Venus in Furs* about an affair between a weak, ineffectual man and a domineering woman. The German sexologist Baron Richard von Krafft-Ebbing (1840–1902) borrowed his name to describe a type of sexual PERVERSION in which someone gets sexual pleasure from being physically hurt or humiliated. Psycho-analysts see masochism as a tendency to turn natural aggressions inwards towards the self rather than taking them out on others.

There is probably a bit of the masochist in everyone and it's sometimes mixed with SADISM (see also SADO-MASOCHISM). In a sexual relationship this is perfectly normal and harmless as long as both partners enjoy it as a game and it doesn't turn into something that causes any real suffering.

massage parlour

As a modern version of what were called 'stews' in medieval times, many of these establishments offer sexual services to men as well as a sauna and a massage. These services usually include 'hand relief' massage, meaning that the female masseur MASTURBATES the customer. For an extra fee the women may agree to have SEXUAL INTER-COURSE.

masturbation

From the Latin for 'defile with the hand', masturbation means stroking or rubbing your CLITORIS or PENIS with your hand for sexual pleasure to achieve an ORGASM. The American film-maker Woody Allen once defined it as making love to someone you really like. It is also something you can do to your partner.

When a girl strokes her GENITALS, especially her clitoris, she begins to feel sexually excited. Her clitoris starts to feel hard and sometimes her VAGINA produces a fluid which makes her external sex organs or VULVA a bit wet (see LUBRICANT). As the excitement increases, the muscles in her vagina begin to tense up and relax until she reaches orgasm and the feelings of pleasure, release of tension and satisfaction all mingle.

A boy experiences much the same feelings by stroking or rubbing his penis, especially at the place where the GLANS joins the main shaft. This movement gives him an ERECTION and a sense of growing sexual excitement. When he reaches orgasm SEMEN comes out from the opening in the tip of his penis in several spurts. His penis then goes limp.

Masturbating can cause absolutely no harm – although you wouldn't think so from all the myths and fears that surround it. It used to be called 'self-pollution' or 'self-abuse', which suggests people thought of it as a misuse of the body. The old word for masturbation was 'onanism' from the character in the Old Testament:

'And Onan knew that the seed should not be his; and it came to pass, when he went in unto his brother's wife, that he spilled it on the ground, lest that he should give seed to his brother.' (Genesis 39:9)

It sounds if Onan withdrew his penis rather than masturbated, explaining why 'onanism' has also meant COITUS INTERRUPTUS.

The early Christian Church definitely didn't approve of sex unless it took place between a married couple and only then in order to have a baby. Since people masturbate for pleasure and it can't get anyone pregnant, it was thought to be sinful. This is still the view of the Roman Catholic Church. Only a little over a hundred years ago, some children who were found masturbating had their arms bound to their sides and their thighs blistered with hot irons. Some boys were CIRCUMCISED (not that this prevents a boy from getting pleasure from masturbating) and some girls had their clitoris removed (see CLITORIDECTOMY) which would have prevented them from getting any sexual pleasure.

Old beliefs linger on. But there is absolutely no evidence to support the myths and jokes which suggest masturbation can make you blind, drive you mad, make hairs grow on the palms of your hands, enlarge or shrink the size of your sex organs, give you stomach aches, dry you up or make you weak.

Couples who practise SAFER SEX often masturbate each other; it's one of the ways of giving and receiving pleasure without running a risk of getting HIV, the virus that can lead to AIDS.

Slang terms for masturbation include bang the bishop, beat one's dummy, log or meat, beat off, beat the hog, bring oneself off, choke the gopher, cuff one's meat, flog one's meat, flong one's dong, a hand job, jerk one's gherkin, jerk off, play with oneself, pound one's meat, pound one's peenie, pull oneself off, pull one's pud, rub off, stroke, toss off, wank or wank off, and whack off.

These are mostly terms used by men and involve the penis rather than the clitoris. This may be because fewer women than men seem to masturbate. Most children are discouraged from touching their genitals, but because a boy has to hold his when he pees he may learn how to masturbate more easily than a girl.

mate

In the fourteenth century 'mate' meaning 'companion or fellow worker' was a common way among sailors and labourers of addressing an equal. It later developed another sense of 'one of a pair' – often birds or the person you married. As a verb, 'to mate' came to mean SEXUAL INTERCOURSE.

meat

Food, sex and love have always had strong associations. Someone who is thought sexy or attractive might be described as 'good enough to eat'. A sexy man may be referred to as 'BEEFCAKE' and a sexy woman as 'CHEESECAKE'. The HYMEN is called a 'CHERRY' and the VAGINA or its owner is known as a 'HONEYPOT'. The TESTICLES are called 'nuts' and a PENIS can be a 'weenie' which is short for a type of sausage. The Black North American slang term 'jelly-roll' has been used for a number of different sexual things such as vagina, a man obsessed by sex, a lover of either sex, sexual activity in general, a woman considered sexually attractive and SEXUAL INTER-COURSE. 'To eat' is a slang term for ORAL SEX.

In a sexual sense 'meat' usually means human female flesh, although as well as having been a vulgar term for the VULVA since the sixteenth century it's also been slang for the penis. The phrase 'a bit of meat' emerged in the eighteenth century as a term used by males for sexual intercourse. A hundred years later it was slang for a PROSTITUTE. A BROTHEL was known as a 'meat-house'. A prostitute new to her trade was called 'fresh meat'. 'Dark meat', a racist term for a Black woman seen as a SEX OBJECT is still sometimes used. The feminist Germaine Greer makes the point that behind the use of 'meat' for a woman is the notion that they are only regarded as dead bits of flesh whose sole purpose is to be eaten by men.

ménage à trois (men-ahj ah twah)

This French phrase means 'household of three'. It's used for an arrangement involving a couple and another lover of either sex who all live and have sex together.

menarche (men-ar-key)

The 'men' part of this word comes from the Latin for month; 'arche' comes from the Greek for 'beginning'. It's the medical term for a girl's first PERIOD which occurs when she reaches PUBERTY.

menopause

'Pause' comes from the Latin word meaning to stop completely and 'meno' from the Latin for month. This is the time in a woman's life, usually from her mid- to late forties or early fifties, when her PERIODS become irregular and eventually stop altogether. This means she is no longer FERTILE and cannot have children. Other terms for it are 'the time of life', 'the change', and CLIMACTERIC.

Both psychologically and physically it can be a disturbing time. The HORMONES in a woman's body change and as a result a woman may experience uncomfortable hot flushes or flashes, a lower level of vaginal LUBRICATION and intense mood swings. Some women take Hormone Replacement Therapy (HRT) for some of the more unpleasant or uncomfortable effects of their menopause and to prevent a bone-thinning condition called osteoporosis.

It doesn't help that we live in a society that values a woman in terms of her youth and fertility. When a girl has her first period she's often told, 'You're a woman now'; but this doesn't mean that a female whose periods have stopped is no longer a woman.

The menopause, like so much about the natural happenings to a woman's body, is seldom talked about. This means that many teenagers don't know why their mother gets snappy and depressed. But it doesn't have to be all bad; as one woman put it, 'The end of periods and birth control. What a relief!'

menses/menstrual cycle/menstruation

In Latin *menses* means 'month'. These are all the formal or medical terms for what are popularly called periods. (See PERIOD for more detail.)

merkin

In the eighteenth century this was a pubic wig worn by those who wanted to disguise the fact that they'd had their PUBIC HAIR shaved off when being treated for a VENEREAL DISEASE. It later came to be used as a term for the female GENITALS or their pubic hair.

mikvah

This is a Hebrew term for the ritual bath that Orthodox Jewish women are expected to take after their PERIOD has finished. Until she's been to the mikvah she is not allowed to have sex with her husband.

mini-pill

There are several different types of the CONTRACEPTIVE pill (see PILL). One sort, which has PROGESTOGEN and no OESTROGEN, is called the Progestogen-Only Pill (POP) or mini-pill. It's mainly recommended for women who are sub-FERTILE or who are advised against taking oestrogen because they are over forty-five, because they smoke heavily, are breast-feeding or have diabetes or slightly high blood pressure. It works by making the mucus inside the VAGINA around the CERVIX thicker. This prevents SPERM from getting into the WOMB and from there into the FALLOPIAN TUBES where one may FERTILIZE an EGG CELL and a baby will be conceived (see CONCEPTION).

It is not as safe as the ordinary pill; if you forget to take one you need to take extra contraceptive precautions if you have sex within the next forty-eight hours.

miscarriage

In medical terms, this is known as a spontaneous ABORTION. When a woman miscarries, the FOETUS is expelled from her WOMB before it has reached its full stage of development. It is estimated that between ten and twenty per cent of all PREGNANCIES end in miscarriage.

The most common reason for miscarriage is something wrong with the development of the foetus; if the foetus dies during pregnancy it ceases to produce the hormones that keep pregnancy going, and the UTERUS automatically empties itself. The trouble may start with an injury to the mother, or an acute illness that also harms the foetus. General ill health or a structural defect can also make it difficult for a woman to stay pregnant.

miscegenation (miss-sej-en-*eh*-shun)

From the Latin *miscere* meaning 'to mix' and *genus* meaning 'race', this means interbreeding between two people of different races and is also widely used to refer to intermarriage between races. The word itself is a perfectly neutral description but it's often used in a condemning way by racists to refer to marriage or sex between black and white people.

missionary position

This position for SEXUAL INTERCOURSE has the woman underneath and the man on top. She lies on her back either with her legs out straight and spread apart or with her knees bent. It got its name because scandalized Victorian missionaries in Polynesia apparently forbade their more uninhibited converts to have sex in any other position.

In the West it's probably the most common of all positions, perhaps because it never occurs to many people to have sex in any other way or because they think that experimenting with different positions is somehow 'rude' or 'wrong'. This view probably has its roots in a strict Christian attitude which thought of sex in terms of creating children rather than having pleasure.

The missionary position has some advantages and some disadvantages. Being able to see your partner's face is a definite plus. But it's not ideal if his PENIS is fairly small, and it can be uncomfortable or even impossible if she is pregnant or if either partner is very overweight. Many women find it difficult to have an ORGASM when they use this position. Some couples find it improves things if they put a pillow under the woman's bottom.

There are countless different positions. You can do it standing up (a 'knee-trembler'), sitting down, he can enter from the rear ('doggy-fashion'), she can sit in his lap or lie on top of him. Some couples like doing it the same way every time, others like trying out new ones. As long as both you and your partner enjoy it and aren't causing any pain there's no right or wrong way of having sex.

Some really amazing positions are described in the classic EROTIC sex manuals, the KAMA SUTRA and THE PERFUMED GARDEN, for which you would need a high degree of athleticism. *The Joy of Sex* by Alex Comfort is less exotic, but more realistic.

mistress

'Mistress' and 'master' both come from an ancient Indo-European root (see Glossary) for 'great' or 'much'. When 'mistress' first entered the English language in the fourteenth century it meant a woman who was in charge of a child. This is where the term 'school mistress' comes from. But when 'master' gained the sense of 'victorious man', the term 'mistress' began to be used of a woman kept by a man in place of a legal wife. Things improved in the sixteenth century when the word got the meaning of 'a woman who has command over a man's heart; one who is loved and courted by a man; a sweetheart or lady love'.

Today a school mistress is more likely to be called a teacher. This may be partly because many women prefer to use a term which includes both women and men, or perhaps because the word mistress also means a woman who has a sexual relationship with a man she's not married to.

Mittelschmerz (mit-el-shmerts)

This German word means literally 'middle pain'. It is the medical name for the pain some girls and women feel when they OVULATE mid-way between their PERIODS. It's usually no more than a slight twinge or cramp in the lower abdomen or back. However, some experience very bad headaches, gastric pains, sluggishness or, in rare cases, a pain so bad that it feels like appendicitis. It's worth seeing a doctor if this happens although there isn't always a lot that can be done.

molestation

This means having parts of your body, usually the BREASTS or GENITALS, touched, pinched or fondled either by a complete stranger or by a man you know, perhaps a family friend or someone at school or in the workplace. (See LECHEROUS.)

The word originates from the Latin for 'burdensome, annoying'. Because it involves unwanted touching it's a form of INDECENT assault, which is a crime and should be reported.

Girls and women (it tends to be females who are molested by boys or men) who complain about this deeply unpleasant behaviour are often not taken seriously. But, like all forms of sexual HARASSMENT, no one has the right to do anything to you that you don't want them to do. It's up to you to decide who you want to touch you, as well as where and when.

monogamy (mon-og-am-ee)

From the Greek words meaning 'alone' and 'marriage', this is the state of being married to one person at a time. It's now also used about a non-marriage relationship in which both partners are sexually faithful.

mons veneris (*ven*-er-is)

This is Latin for 'mound of Venus'. Venus was the ancient Roman goddess of love. It's a medical term which refers to the soft pad of fatty tissue that covers a female's pubic bone.

morning-after pill/IUD See EMERGENCY CONTRACEPTION and RU 486.

motherfucker

This is widely considered to be one of the most offensive terms in the English language. At one point in its history 'mother' was slang for a PROSTITUTE or a MADAM who ran a BROTHEL; today 'mother' is also American slang for a PIMP and for the most attractive member of a group of HOMOSEXUALS. But the 'mother' in 'mother-fucker' seems to be a reference to the woman who gives birth to you. 'FUCK' has different meanings too − it can mean 'to cheat', for example − but here it means SEXUAL INTERCOURSE. At some level, therefore, a motherfucker implies an INCESTUOUS sexual relationship between a mother and her son, although it's never used literally in this way. It's mostly used of anyone who is thought to be really mean, nasty, or who is totally despised.

The term was originally Black American slang but then became popular among the general male population in the Armed Forces during the Second World War (1939–1945). It was especially popular among black construction workers during the Korean War in the 1950s. Since then 'motherfucker' has gradually begun to replace the terms BASTARD and son of a BITCH. It has various different forms, some used humorously: mother eater, mother dangler, mother flunker, mother grabber, mother helper, mother joker, mother kisser, mother lover, mother nudger, mother pisser, mother rucker, mother sucker, and many more. Sometimes it's shortened to just 'mother'.

In some Catholic countries the mother in 'motherfucker' is a blasphemous reference to the VIRGIN Mary.

multiple orgasm See AFTERPLAY and ORGASM.

N

narcissism

In Greek mythology Narcissus was a handsome young man who despised love. The best-known version of his story is in *Metamorphoses* by the Latin poet Ovid (43 BC–AD 17). The mother of Narcissus, the blue nymph called Liriope, had been told her son would live to a ripe old age provided he never looked at himself. One day Narcissus, a VIRGIN who rejected all women, came across a spring with water as clear as silver. As he lay down to drink he fell in love with his own reflection. He tried to kiss the beautiful young man he saw, but he soon recognized himself and lay gazing at his image for hour after hour. His feelings were a mixture of rapture and pain. Eventually he plunged a dagger into his heart saying, 'Ah, youth, beloved in vain, farewell!' His blood soaked the earth and immediately the white narcissus flower sprang up with its blood-red centre, which has narcotic properties. The word 'narcissus' probably comes from the Greek word meaning 'numbness, stupor'.

The term narcissism was first coined (see Glossary) by psychologists for a sexual PERVERSION in which a woman or man can only get sexually excited or satisfied by their own body. It's used more generally to mean a rather immature or neurotic love of oneself.

necrophilia (nekro-*fill*-ee-ah)

From the Greek *nekro* meaning 'corpse' and 'philia' meaning 'loving', this is an extreme but rare psychosexual disorder (see PERVERSION) which involves getting sexual excitement and satisfaction from contact with dead bodies.

nipple

It was once thought that 'nipple' was connected to the Old English word *nypel* meaning 'elephant trunk'. Stranger things have happened in the English language, but it's now thought that nipple, once spelled *nible*, comes from the word *nib* meaning 'point'. The medical term is *mamilla*, from the Latin *mamma* meaning BREAST.

Most people think of the nipple as the whole of the dark area of crinkly skin at the tip of the breast. In fact, the nipple is just the pointed bit; the area around it is the AREOLA.

When we're born the nipples of baby girls and boys look much the same. But when a girl reaches PUBERTY her nipples become a darkish brown colour and start to get larger. Some girls have one or two nipples that lie flat or ones that turn in instead of sticking out, called inverted nipples. Sometimes they get pushed out as the breasts get larger but if they don't it doesn't matter. Everyone's nipples are different and all are normal.

When a woman is breast-feeding the baby sucks on the nipple and milk flows through small ducts from the milk-producing glands inside the breast. Special nipple shields are made for those with inverted nipples to make it easier for them to breast-feed their babies.

Nipples become erect when a person feels cold or sexually aroused. Most women and some men enjoy having their nipples touched so much that they can have an ORGASM when someone touches or plays with them. It's thought that more men would realize their nipples were EROGENOUS ZONES if breasts weren't so widely thought of as being a female domain.

nonce

This was originally British prison slang for a man who sexually abuses children – a type of criminal who is particularly despised among prisoners. (See CHILD SEXUAL ABUSE.) Outside prison it gained the sense of a PERVERT and sometimes just an unpleasant and/or stupid person, usually a man.

non-gonococcal or non-specific urethritis

Often shortened to NGU or NSU, this is an inflammation of the URETHRA most often caused by the CHLAMYDIA bacteria. It affects both females and males and, along with GONORRHOEA, it is one of the most common SEXUALLY TRANSMITTED DISEASES. It can be spread by SEXUAL INTERCOURSE, by ANAL SEX, and by FELLATIO during ORAL SEX.

The symptoms are very similar to those of CYSTITIS – wanting to pee very frequently and a burning feeling when you do pee. Unlike cystitis it's usually accompanied by a discharge from the CERVIX or PENIS. Some people, however, have no symptoms at all.

If you or your partner get any of these symptoms you should go to your doctor or to a SPECIAL CLINIC. You will probably be checked for gonorrhoea as well. Penicillin, which cures gonorrhoea, doesn't cure NGU/NSU so you'll be prescribed another antibiotic. You shouldn't have sex until you have been told that you are completely cured.

Nonoxynol 9

This chemical is present in most SPERMICIDAL creams and jellies. It destroys on contact both SPERM and HIV, the virus that can lead to AIDS. When practising SAFER SEX it's a very good idea to use both a CONDOM and a spermicide containing Nonoxynol 9 (or octoxynol). But it's not 100 per cent effective since the virus can enter parts of VAGINA that the spermicide hasn't reached. It also causes irritation in a large number of people.

nymphet (nim-*fet*)

A nymphet (or nymphette) is a sexually attractive girl – often one who is below the AGE OF CONSENT. In his novel LOLITA, Vladimir Nabokov (1899–1977) defined a nymphet like this:

'Between the age limits of nine and fourteen there occur maidens who, to certain bewitched travellers twice or many times older than they, reveal their true nature which is not human, but nymphic (that is, demoniac); and these chosen creatures I propose to designate as nymphets.'

(See CHILD SEXUAL ABUSE and STATUTORY RAPE.)

In Greek mythology, the nymphs were beautiful and often alluring young women who were associated with aspects of nature such as seas, rivers, mountains, forests and trees. Some were the handmaidens of the goddesses and gods. The inner lips (or LABIA) of the female outer sex organs came to be called 'nymphae' – a term which is now obsolete (see Glossary). Another sense of the Greek word was 'bride'.

nympholepsy

A nympholept is someone who is inspired by violent enthusiasm for a cause or ideal. It comes from a Greek word meaning 'caught by nymphs' (see NYMPHET). Nympholepsy comes from this word and it means sexual ecstasy or frenzy caused by desiring what can never be achieved.

nymphomaniac (nim-fo-*main*-ee-ak)

This word is based on the Greek words for 'bride' (see NYMPHET) and 'madness'. Psychiatrists in the nineteenth century believed nymphomania was a disorder suffered by women who couldn't control their sexual desire. One 'cure' was thought to be the removal of the woman's CLITORIS (see CLITORIDECTOMY). The male version was called SATYRIASIS but this was never treated as an illness. Today, many psychiatrists doubt if nymphomania, as an illness, has ever really existed. There is, however, an extremely rare female psychological disorder in which a woman becomes sexually aroused but never has an ORGASM.

The word 'nympho' is often used whenever a female seems to like sex or wants to express her sexual feelings. It's become an inaccurate term to describe a girl or woman who is sexually PROMISCUOUS. There's definitely a DOUBLE STANDARD operating here as the American feminist writer Gloria Steinem pointed out:

'Nymphomania ... was mainly used to condemn any woman who made more sexual demands than one man could handle ... The sexually aggressive woman [since the 1960s] is a SLUT or a nymphomaniac, but the sexually aggressive man is just normal.'

O

obscene (ob-*seen*)

There has been a long debate about where the word obscene comes from. Because of some of the rude jokes played by actors in ancient Roman times who wore large stuffed leather PENISES it's been suggested that the Latin word *scena*, meaning stage, might be the original source. The Victorian sexologist Havelock-Ellis thought it might have once meant 'off the scene', referring to things that were too rude to appear or be said in front of an audience. It may come from the Latin word *caenum*, meaning dirt, filth, mire or FAECES. The word *obscenus* was used by Roman fortune-tellers meaning 'ill-omened, abominable, disgusting, INDECENT, ugly, IMMORAL, revolting'.

When 'obscenity' first entered English in the sixteenth century it meant something that offended the senses, i.e. smell, sight, sound, taste and touch. In general speech today 'obscene' means 'loathsome' or anything that offends an idea of what is thought to be morally right. So you might hear someone say that the refusal of rich countries to help starving people in poor countries is obscene. But mostly it's used in a sexual context. The American Law Institute defines obscenity as anything that caters above all for INDECENCY – a shameful, morbid interest in nudity, in the GENITALS, or in faeces, for instance. The British legal definition of obscenity is a book, magazine, painting or film that supposedly depraves and corrupts.

The legal arguments about defining obscenity are part of a wider argument about defining what is PORNOGRAPHY and what is EROTIC literature or art. Some people believe that anything that shows in pictures or words the sexual act or naked women and men, can have the effect of making the reader or viewer do something sexually depraved or causes them to corrupt others who are innocent. The counter-argument is that these people must have been interested in the first place, so the material didn't have any effect on them. It is left to the law courts to decide whether or not such material should be censored or banned.

Attitudes about what is obscene differ the world over and often change over a period of time. At one time the USA's obscenity laws made it illegal to send through the post a reproduction of the painting of a naked woman called *La Maja* by the great Spanish artist Goya. Catholic Spain, meanwhile, used this 'obscenity' on a stamp. At the beginning of the twentieth century, books and pamphlets advising on BIRTH CONTROL were judged to be obscene, yet in the 1980s governments throughout the world were spending money advertising CONDOMS.

Famous books that have been prosecuted on charges of obscenity in the twentieth century include *LADY CHATTERLEY'S LOVER* by D. H. Lawrence; Radclyffe Hall's *The Well of Loneliness*, one of the first popular novels about a LESBIAN relationship; *Ulysses*, the masterpiece by the Irish novelist James Joyce; *The Tropic of Cancer* by the American writer Henry Miller. All are now considered classic works of literature and are available in most bookshops.

obscene phone call

Most obscene phone calls are made by inadequate males who probably MASTURBATE while they are talking dirty, or breathing heavily to a stranger (usually a girl or woman) on the phone. It can be very frightening, especially if you're alone in the house. Although very few obscene callers are actually dangerous, there's always the fear that the caller might know your address and come round in person. Making dirty phone calls is a criminal act. They should be reported to the police. You can also report it to the phone company which may be able to trace the caller and will give you a new phone number.

Oedipus complex (eed-ee-puss)

Oedipus the King is the title of a play by Sophocles, who was born in Athens in 496 BC. The plot tells the tragic story of King Oedipus who is abandoned by his parents as a baby and who later discovers that unknowingly he had murdered his father Laius, and married his mother Jocasta. Learning of the relationship with her son (see INCEST), Jocasta commits suicide and Oedipus blinds himself.

Sigmund Freud, the founder of psychoanalysis, believed the Oedipus myth was universal, that is, present in all of us. He used the myth to explain the sexual development of the individual. Between the ages of three and four, boys become especially emotionally close to their mothers and try to push their fathers away. Girls experience the opposite. Both experience with enormous intensity the emotions of love, hate, rivalry and jealousy that are all present in the Oedipal drama. The term 'Oedipus complex' is used to describe someone (usually male) who gets stuck at this stage of their development; they remain too close to their mother and have a very difficult relationship with their father, which results in neurotic symptoms in later life. Freud believed the Oedipus complex plays a fundamental part in structuring our personality and influencing our sexual orientation. (See HETEROSEXUAL, HOMOSEXUAL, BISEXUAL.)

oestrogen (*ees*-tro-jen)
This is the name for the female HORMONE which controls OVULATION. It gets its name from a Greek word meaning 'gadfly, frenzy, mad with desire'. A gadfly is one of several types of flies that bite or annoy livestock, and a term for an annoying person who stimulates or provokes others by persistent criticism. This presumably drives the victim into a frenzy. Made in the OVARIES, oestrogen is the hormone most responsible for bringing about sexual maturity – growth of PUBIC HAIR and BREASTS, MENSTRUATION and so on – when a girl reaches PUBERTY.

From the age of about twenty-five the amount of oestrogen produced in the ovaries begins to decline as glands just above the kidneys (called adrenal glands) gradually take over, until they become the major source of oestrogen after a woman reaches MENOPAUSE and she stops ovulating.

Artificial oestrogen is one of the main ingredients of the PILL, and of the drugs used for HRT (Hormone Replacement Therapy) which can treat some of the problems women suffer from during the menopause.

Boys also produce oestrogen but it is not a dominant male hormone.

on the job
In the sixteenth century the verb 'to job' meant to have SEXUAL INTERCOURSE, possibly a joke on the idea of sex as a duty that wives and husbands had to perform in order to have children. In the mid-nineteenth century, 'to do a woman's job for her' was an expression used by men for making sure a woman experienced pleasure during sex. Towards the end of the nineteenth century the phrase 'on the job' meant both to be honest or genuine and to work quickly and steadily. 'A job' is also criminal slang for a burglary or other crime.

Sex may be a duty or even hard work for some people but anyone who describes their sexual experience as a job doesn't sound as if they're getting – or giving – much pleasure.

oral contraceptive
This is a term for any contraceptive that is 'taken by mouth'. See PILL and MINI-PILL.

oral sex
From the Latin for 'of the mouth', this means the sort of sex in which the GENITALS (VAGINA or PENIS) are stimulated by the tongue or lips by KISSING, licking or sucking. FELLATIO is the name given to oral stimulation of the penis; CUNNILINGUS means oral stimulation of the vagina and/or CLITORIS. The position in which a couple lie head to toe, with both using their mouths on their partner's sex organs is called '*soixante-neuf*'. Some people like it if their partner uses their tongue and mouth to stimulate the area around the ANUS. This is known as anilingus.

You can't become pregnant from oral sex but many SEXUALLY TRANSMITTED DISEASES, including GONORRHOEA and HERPES, can be passed on this way. Because SEMEN, the vaginal juices, MENSTRUAL blood, and saliva can all contain HIV, there may be some risk attached to oral sex. The risk is greater if a partner has bleeding gums, mouth ulcers or any cuts or sores in their mouth.

Couples who enjoy cunnilingus and fellatio and who practise SAFER SEX use a CONDOM on the penis and a DENTAL DAM on the VULVA. RIMMING, a term for mouth to anus sex, carries a high risk of several diseases including HIV and HEPATITIS and so is not a safer sex practice.

Most of us are brought up to believe that our sex organs are dirty (jokes about sex are often called 'dirty'), so the idea of oral sex can seem quite horrible at first. But many couples find it a very loving way of expressing their feelings for one another. As with all things related to sex, don't do it if it doesn't appeal to you and never force your partner to do something he or she doesn't like.

orgasm (*or*-gazm)

This comes from a Greek word which means 'to swell' and 'to be excited'. This mixture of something that happens to your body and to your mind is pretty much what it's like to have an orgasm. It's the point when you reach the peak, or CLIMAX, of sexual excitement and you're so swollen up with pleasure that it feels like you're going to burst. These waves of intense pleasure are followed by relaxation. You can have an orgasm either by MASTURBATING or by having sex with a partner. You don't necessarily have to have SEXUAL INTERCOURSE to have one.

Having an orgasm follows a similar pattern for both females and males. First of all we get sexually aroused (see FOREPLAY). As a woman's CLITORIS is stimulated by being touched, stroked or kissed it starts to swell, as do her LABIA (see TUMESCENCE). Her VAGINA may produce some juices (see LUBRICANT) which make her sex organs feel warm and slippery. Her climax involves a series of short rhythmic spasms of the vagina which spread to the WOMB and the whole body. In a male, the PENIS swells when it is stimulated and he gets an ERECTION. As the stimulation continues the sensation of sexual pleasure increases until he reaches the point when he EJACULATES, and SEMEN comes shooting out of the end of his penis in several spurts.

After an orgasm it takes a woman a bit of time to 'come down' and she may be able to have another one or two (or more) immediately after, called multiple orgasms. A man finds that his penis goes back to its normal size almost immediately after and it usually takes him a bit longer before he can COME again.

Males who claim they can come time after time are making it up.

Sometimes lovers feel a bit sorrowful after having an orgasm; it's called *post-coitum triste* (Latin for 'sad after COITUS'). Other times they might feel relaxed, happy and satisfied. No two people are alike in the feelings and sensations they experience and no two orgasms are exactly the same. You don't necessarily have one every time you have sexual intercourse. It can be FRUSTRATING to get excited and then not come — but sex, when it's good, is about sharing and caring, giving and taking, and not about achieving orgasms.

orgy (*or*-jee)

To most people an orgy is a wild party at which there's lots of sex. They might also be referring to an indulgent bout of drinking and eating. In ancient Greece, however, the word meant 'secret worship' which involved sexual rites. The fifth-century BC Greek philosopher Plato referred to an orgy as the 'divine frenzy'. Christianity put an end to such forms of worship and the word entered the English language in the eighteenth century to mean a LICENTIOUS revel.

ovary (*oh*-var-ee)

Based on the Latin word for 'egg', the ovaries are the primary female reproductive organs. Every female has two almond-shaped ovaries, each of which stores several hundred thousand immature EGG CELLS. Once she reaches PUBERTY, one egg cell matures to form an OVUM approximately once a month (see OVULATION). This is due to HORMONES produced in the ovaries called OESTROGEN and PROGESTERONE.

ovulation (ov-u-*lay*-shon)

From the Greek word for 'egg', ovulation is the moment when an OVUM is released from one of the OVARIES. It starts happening on a monthly basis when a girl reaches PUBERTY and continues until a woman reaches MENOPAUSE. When it happens a girl or woman may feel some pain, which the medical profession calls MITTELSCHMERZ.

ovum (*oh*-vum)

This is a Latin word meaning egg (the plural is ova). An ovum is the mature female reproductive cell (see GAMETE) stored in immature form (called EGG CELLS) in the OVARIES. Released from an ovary at OVULATION, if an ovum is FERTILIZED by a SPERM in a FALLOPIAN TUBE a new life is formed. All unfertilized ova are shed during a menstrual PERIOD.

P

paedophilia (pee-doh-*fill*-ee-a)

The 'paedo' part of this word comes from the Greek for 'boy, child'; 'philia' is from the Greek for 'friendly, dear'. In the English language a word ending in 'philia' can mean 'a tendency towards' and 'an exaggerated or abnormal fondness or liking for something'.

Paedophilia is the sexual love of children. A paedophile is someone who feels sexual desire for children. Many people are wrongly convinced that most HOMOSEXUALS are paedophiles but by far the largest proportion are HETEROSEXUAL men who are attracted to young girls. Very few women appear to suffer from this psychosexual disorder.

There are different degrees of paedophilia. A paedophile like Lewis Carroll, the Victorian author of *Alice in Wonderland* who took photographs of naked young girls, confined his paedophile desire to VOYEURISM and FANTASY. Others, such as the Russian novelist Fyodor Dostoyevsky, had SEXUAL INTERCOURSE with children. The society we live in has confused thoughts on the subject. On the one hand, the sexual ABUSE of children is treated as a crime and on the other, many young girls are dressed up in sexy clothes – you quite often see them at children's talent shows or on TV commercials – and are thought to be 'cute'. (See LOLITA, NYMPHET.)

Children need to be protected from child molesters (see MOLESTATION) and given help to cope with the emotional disturbance that inevitably follows from being abused by adults. Psychiatrists believe that paedophiles need help too – there is no evidence to show that sending them to prison cures them or stops them from doing it again.

page-three girl

In the mid-1970s the British tabloid newspaper, *The Sun*, started to print photos of topless models on page three. This proved to be highly popular among male readers and circulation zoomed, forcing other tabloid papers to copy (although not necessarily on page three).

The topless models who appear in newspapers are women, often in their twenties, but are referred to as 'girls' – perhaps because many men appear to think of a girl as being easier to dominate and control and therefore more sexy than a mature woman. Many women dislike these photos and a campaign to introduce a law banning these photos received huge support, but no law was passed because of insufficient support from the predominantly male Parliament. The phrase 'doing a page three' is now slang in the UK for 'to appear topless in public'. A 'page three girl' (who may also be referred to as a BIMBO) means any model prepared to expose her BREASTS and has almost taken over from the earlier term 'PIN-UP girl'.

pansy

In the 1930s pansy emerged as a popular word to mean either an EFFEMINATE boy or man, or a male HOMOSEXUAL. It's an insulting term used mainly by those who hate or fear homosexuality.

People who wrongly believe that a male GAY isn't a real man often use the name of a flower to make him feel inadequate because flowers are thought to be 'FEMININE'. Similar slang words used for gays or men who aren't MACHO include daisy, jessie (from jasmine), lily and flower.

Pap smear See CERVICAL SMEAR TEST.

paramour (*par*-ra-moor)

In French, *par amour* literally means 'by way of love'. Originally it meant an illicit lover perhaps because until the seventeenth century most marriages were about property rather than love. Like many words related to sex, it later lost its wider meaning and became connected only with the female sex and is now an obsolescent (see Glossary) word for a MISTRESS.

There aren't many suitable words to describe the person you live with and/or love. Girlfriend and boyfriend are fine when you're young but sound fairly silly for anyone over the age of thirty. Lover sounds a bit too intimate. A mistress suggests a woman who is paid money for her sexual services. A term like 'meaningful other' gets used in the USA but most people think it sounds rather artificial, while 'partner' sounds more like a business associate. The Spanish get over the problem without embarrassment with the words '*companera*' (female) and '*companero*' (male) which mean a mixture of companion and lover.

pass

'To make a pass' was originally a 1920s American colloquialism (see Glossary) to describe the first step taken by a male to SEDUCE a woman. The phrase was made famous by the witty American writer Dorothy Parker (1893–1967) who wrote: 'Men seldom make passes at girls who wear glasses.'

paternity test

From the Latin word *pater*, meaning 'father', this refers to a blood test which can help establish the identity of a child's father. Under English law a single mother is automatically her child's only legal guardian and the father has no automatic rights over the child he believes to be his. Nor does he have any legal responsibilities if he denies he is the father.

Paternity is not easy to prove. Samples of blood are taken from both the baby and the boy or man who is thought to be its father. The test can only prove either that he is definitely not the father or, if the two blood groups are compatible, that he might be the father. It can't prove that he definitely is the father. If he refuses to take this test the court will probably assume he is the father and order him to pay maintenance.

pederast (*ped*-er-ast)

This comes from the Greek word meaning 'lover of boys'. In English it means a man who has ANAL SEX with a boy. People who are quick to condemn all forms of HOMOSEXUALITY (see HOMOPHOBIA) often appear to think that all male gays are likely to ABUSE boys (see PAEDOPHILIA) but this is far from the truth – most gays, like most HETEROSEXUALS, choose other adults for their partners.

pee See URINE.

peeping Tom
This used to mean 'an inquisitive person', from the eleventh century legend about Lady Godiva whose husband promised tax relief to the people if she agreed to ride naked on horseback through the streets of Coventry. Apart from a certain tailor named Tom, the rest of the townsfolk all politely shut their eyes. Today 'peeping Tom' is a common term for a VOYEUR.

pelvic examination
Also called an internal examination, a doctor sometimes needs to feel inside a girl's or woman's VAGINA to check her internal reproductive organs which lie within the cavity of her pelvic bone. She will undress from the waist down and lie on the examining couch with her knees bent and spread apart. Some clinics have stirrups placed at the end of the couch for her to put her feet into. The doctor wears a pair of thin plastic gloves and places one hand at the base of her abdomen just above the pubic bone, inserts two fingers inside the vagina, and gently presses the pelvic area from both inside and outside. The doctor may also do a rectal examination in order to feel the organs better. This involves inserting a finger into the ANUS. They will be looking for any unusual swelling, soreness or lumps.

She or he (there should be a professional female health worker present if the doctor is a male) will also use a special instrument called a SPECULUM which they insert into the vagina to help them see the CERVIX. They will then do a CERVICAL SMEAR TEST, (also called a pap smear) using a long cotton bud-like stick to gently scrape some cell tissue from the cervix.

Many girls and women think having a pelvic exam is undignified and embarrassing. They're not particularly comfortable but, if performed correctly, they shouldn't hurt.

pelvic inflammatory disease (PID)

This is the general name for various diseases and infections inside a girl's or woman's body in the pelvic area which is the area inside her lower abdomen containing her reproductive organs. Symptoms of PID can include very severe cramps whether or not she's having her PERIOD, irregular bleeding, general pelvic pain sometimes with a chill or fever. It can be caused by a SEXUALLY TRANSMITTED DISEASE, especially GONORRHOEA, or a perforated womb resulting from an IUD. Treatment for PID is a course of antibiotics, time off work or school for lots of rest, and no SEXUAL INTERCOURSE for at least two weeks.

penetrative sex

This term means any sexual activity in which the PENIS enters into the VAGINA, ANUS, or mouth. (See SEXUAL INTERCOURSE, ANAL SEX, and ORAL SEX.)

Many women think penetrative sex isn't a particularly imaginative way of enjoying sex. Making love doesn't always depend on the need for the male partner to get an ERECTION and perform every time. Girls and women can be sexually satisfied in many ways other than having a penis inside them.

In terms of SAFER SEX, penetrative sex carries a high risk of spreading SEXUALLY TRANSMITTED DISEASES including HIV, the virus that can lead to AIDS. The risk is reduced if one partner always wears a CONDOM and the other uses a SPERMICIDE containing NONOXYNOL 9. Some couples have decided that penetrative sex is too risky and they bring each other to ORGASM by kissing, stroking and massaging each other, and by mutual MASTURBATION.

penile (*pee*-nile)

An adjective meaning 'of or relating to the PENIS'.

penis

This Latin word for the male sex organ also meant 'tail' and in the fourteenth century 'tail' became a slang term for a penis. 'Tail' also used to refer to the female sex organs (see TAIL).

The penis is made up of two parts. The long part is known as the shaft and the head is called the GLANS. Where the glans meets the shaft there is a thickish fold of skin, called the FORESKIN which covers the glans when it is limp (see DETUMESCENCE). At the very tip of the penis is an opening to a tube called the URETHRA. Right up inside the penis this tube branches into two smaller tubes. One goes to the bladder where URINE collects and the other to the internal sex organs where SEMEN and SPERM are produced and stored. There is a tiny valve which ensures that a boy or man can't pee and EJACULATE at the same time.

The penis is made of spongy, or erectile, tissue which has many small blood vessels in it. When it's limp and flaccid, blood flows through the penis at a steady rate. When he gets sexually excited a ring of muscle inside the base of the shaft tightens, allowing blood to flow in but not out. This makes the penis grow ERECT (see TUMESCENCE). As sexual excitement dies down (after an ORGASM, for example), the muscle ring relaxes and the penis reverts back to its normal size.

Most males worry at some time or another about the size of their penis. Despite all rumours (and boasts) most penises are more or less the same size: about two or three inches when limp and about five to six inches when erect. Like all averages, some are a bit smaller and others a bit larger. There's absolutely nothing anyone can do to make it bigger and there isn't any need either because the amount of sexual pleasure that a man feels or gives his partner has very little to do with size.

Some slang terms suggest that males see their penis as a good friend (see DICK, JACK, JOHN), others seem to make a connection between food and sex and some show an association with crime.

Slang terms include bayonet, beef, belongings, bicho (Latino slang), bone (there are no bones inside the penis), business (see ON THE JOB), cherry-splitter (see VIRGINITY), club, dang, dibble, dick, dicky, ding-dong (both females and males use the expression 'ring my bell' meaning 'touch my penis/clitoris'), dong, doodle, dork, dummy, flute ('play me a tune' is about ORAL SEX), hairsplitter (a reference to the PUBIC HAIR of a girl or woman), hammer, hog, horn, hose, hunk of MEAT, jang, jigger, jock, John, Johnny, johnson, John Thomas, joint, jones, joy knob, joy stick, knob, love-muscle, meat, member (an old fashioned way of mentioning the penis without actually using the word was the Latin term *membrum virile* which translates as 'male member'), middle leg, one-eyed, trouser snake (Australian), pecker, peenie, Percy, Peter, poker, pole, pork, prick, prong, pud, putz, ramrod, reamer, rod, root, sausage, schmuck, schlong, short arm, skin flute, sugar stick, third leg, tool, tummy banana (made popular by the Australian comic-strip character, Barry McKenzie in the 1960s) wang, weener, weenie (presumably a pun on both 'wee wee', a child's term for URINE, and 'wee' the Scottish word for small), weiner (see MEAT), Willy, works, yang, yard (clearly a boast), ying-yang.

Other euphemisms (see Glossary) include terms which are used for something you don't know the name for such as dingbat, dingus, doodad, dofunny, dojigger, thingy, thingummy.

The Perfumed Garden

Written sometime around the mid-sixteenth century by the Sheik Umar ibn Muhammed al-Nefzawi, *The Perfumed Garden* is a famous Arabic book which is partly a sex manual and partly erotic literature. Although it is written from a man's point of view and women are not very highly regarded, it reveals the Muslim view of this period that sex should be equally pleasurable to both women and men. Nothing as sexually liberated or as erotically beautiful as this book was written in the so-called 'civilized' Western world at this time or, perhaps, ever since.

period

This is the most widely used term for MENSTRUATION or the MENSES. It gets called 'period' from the period of time during which a girl or woman bleeds. A period can last from about three to six days and occurs about every twenty-eight days. The menstrual cycle is calculated from the first day of the period. OVULATION happens about fourteen days later at the mid-point of the cycle. But very few women are absolutely regular and periods can vary from month to month.

The period itself (formally called the menstrual flow) consists of blood, mucus, and the discarded lining (see ENDOMETRIUM) of the WOMB. During a period SANITARY TOWELS or TAMPONS are used to absorb the flow.

Girls and women get their periods from PUBERTY until they have finished their MENOPAUSE – unless they are PREGNANT or have just had a baby, are very underweight, are ill, or have some problem with their reproductive system. Eating disorders such as anorexia nervosa and bulimia can also stop a girl or woman from menstruating (see AMENORRHOEA). For pain associated with periods see DYSMENOR-RHOEA and PREMENSTRUAL TENSION.

Although having a period is a positive sign of fertility and health the whole subject is something of a TABOO in many societies. People go to great lengths not to mention it openly and often use euphem-isms (see Glossary) when talking about them. 'Period' itself is a euphemism. Most of the other expressions and slang terms suggest that women and men see periods in a negative light; this may be because it was once believed wrongly that a woman couldn't have SEXUAL INTERCOURSE when she had her periods, or because some women do feel unwell either just before or during their period.

Slang terms that have been used over the years include the CURSE, to be sick, ill or unwell, falling off the roof, the flowers (probably mistranslated from the Latin word meaning 'to flow'), female com-plaint, indisposed, on the rag, the (bloody) flag is up, to have a visitor, looks like a wet weekend, on drip, jam butties (a butty is northern English slang for a sandwich), the time of the month, feeling poorly, aunty, a little visitor or friend, the monthlies, red Mary, wallflower week.

permissiveness

Depending on your attitude, permissiveness can either mean an appalling lack of discipline and morality or a wonderfully liberal and tolerant view of sexual matters. The popular song *Anything Goes* written by Cole Porter in the 1930s reflects a positive attitude towards permissiveness: 'In olden days a glimpse of stocking/Was looked upon as something shocking/But now, heaven knows/Anything goes.'

In the 1960s the term 'The Permissive Society' was coined (see Glossary) to describe the sort of atmosphere in which unmarried women began to be allowed birth control, and laws on HOMOSEXUAL-ITY, ABORTION and divorce were made easier. Some people were shocked and talked of the PROMISCUOUS society. Others, like the British poet Philip Larkin, celebrated the new freedoms. The first three verses of his poem entitled *Annus Mirabilis* (miraculous or remarkable year) read:

> Sexual intercourse began
> In nineteen sixty-three
> (Which was rather late for me)
> Between the end of the Chatterley ban
> And the Beatle's first LP.

> Up till then there'd only been
> A sort of bargaining,
> A wrangle for a ring,
> A shame that started at sixteen
> And spread to everything.

> Then all at once the quarrel sank:
> Everyone felt the same,
> And every life became
> A brilliant breaking of the bank,
> A quite unloseable game.

pervert/perversion

The Latin verb *pervertere* means 'to turn round, the wrong way, overturn, ruin, corrupt'. Today, in a sexual sense, 'perversion' means 'different from the norm'. If the norm is seen simply as SEXUAL INTERCOURSE with someone of the opposite sex, then there are an awful lot of people who enjoy what is supposedly 'perverted'. Many prefer to use the softer terms 'variant', 'deviation' or 'aberra-tion' to describe sexual activity that differs from the so-called 'norm' because the word perversion carries with it a hint of sinful-ness and a strong sense of disapproval.

Those who are intolerant of anyone who is not like them may

describe a HOMOSEXUAL, a BISEXUAL, or a TRANSVESTITE as a pervert. Such people certainly differ from the norm but they don't cause any harm and it is needlessly cruel and harmful to call them perverts.

What most people mean when they call someone a pervert (often shortened to 'perv') is that he or she is probably a child molester (see CHILD SEXUAL ABUSE) or can only get sexual pleasure from doing things like having sex with an animal (see BESTIALITY, ZOOPHILIA), by causing pain (see SADISM), or who has a FETISH. A FLASHER or a PEEPING TOM, for instance, is certainly a pervert.

In the world of psychology, perversion is used as a neutral term to describe the practice of someone who can't get sexual satisfaction from heterosexual intercourse and a pervert is someone who needs help from a psychologist. But in most countries perverts are punished rather than given the psychiatric treatment they need.

pessary (*pess*-ar-ee)
From the Greek word for 'oval stone' or 'pebble', a pessary is a device inserted into the VAGINA to prevent a prolapse of the WOMB, or to prevent PREGNANCY (see DIAPHRAGM). A pessary is also a tablet of medicine which has to be inserted into the vagina – often to cure a SEXUALLY TRANSMITTED DISEASE or a vaginal discharge.

Peter
This is one of several male Christian names given to the PENIS. Others include DICK, JOHN, John Thomas, Willy and Percy. A peter-meter is a joke term for an instrument which measures the length of the penis.

petting
The French word *petit*, meaning small, gave the English language the word 'pet', meaning a small, domesticated animal. Presumably because pets were stroked and fondled by their owners, people started to use the word to mean 'a pampered and spoiled child, a darling, a loved one'. From this, the verb 'to pet' came to mean loving, embracing, caressing and KISSING. 'Necking', 'making out' and 'feeling up' are current terms for petting.

phallus (*fal*-luss)

In Greek, this means both 'PENIS' and something that looks like and represents a penis symbolically. In English, people tend to use the word 'penis' for the male sex organ and 'phallus' for the symbol, although technically 'phallus' can mean both. A maypole is a good example of a phallic symbol – planted in 'Mother Earth' it stands up erect on a village green representing a man's sexual powers. The Latin for phallus is *fascinum* which had a related meaning of 'magical spirit' and is the source of the word 'fascinate'.

In psychoanalytic theory the phallic stage in a young boy's life is when he becomes preoccupied with his penis and with ideas of manliness, potency, strength and power. According to Sigmund Freud, young girls become aware they don't have a penis and experience 'penis envy'. Freud's tendency to see girls in this way has been criticized for being 'phallocentric' because it regards girls as sub-standard boys.

The phallic woman or mother is another psychoanalytic term which means a dream or fantasy image of a woman with a penis or one who has phallic powers. This image can be seen in many films in which the female star wears tight-fitting sheath-type dresses, so that her body looks like an erect penis, and behaves in a somewhat masculine or authoritarian manner. The 1930s film star, Mae West, and Madonna in the film *Dick Tracy* are examples of the phallic woman.

pheromone

Based on the Greek word meaning 'convey' and on 'hormone', this is a hormonal substance that usually gives off a scent. It's secreted by many animals, and possibly by humans, to stimulate and attract another member of the same species, usually of the opposite sex.

philanderer

The 'phil' part of this word means 'loving' from the Greek for 'dear, friendly'. The last part is based on the Greek word meaning 'man' in the sense of male. Originally 'philander' may have meant a HOMO-SEXUAL. However, because Philander was a stock name for a male HETEROSEXUAL lover in medieval romances and plays, the verb 'to philander' came to mean 'to flirt, play around with a woman's affections'. It's not a word that gets used much these days but a philanderer is now a slightly negative term for a man who has many affairs and treats his women very casually. (See also CASANOVA, DON JUAN, LOTHARIO, PLAYBOY.)

the pill

The oral contraceptive pill is usually referred to as 'the pill'. There are many different sorts but basically all contain two artificial HORMONES: OESTROGEN and PROGESTOGEN. The MINI-PILL contains progestogen only.

The pill is the most reliable form of CONTRACEPTION. It prevents an EGG CELL from ripening in the OVARY which means that OVULATION doesn't take place. Without a mature egg (OVUM), FERTILIZATION and, therefore, PREGNANCY is impossible. It doesn't stop a girl or woman from having her PERIOD each month (it's always totally regular for women taking the pill) although many notice that their periods become much lighter.

It has to be prescribed by a doctor who will work out which type is the right one. Some produce unwanted side effects such as headaches, weight gain or irritability. Girls who have a family history of heart disease, BREAST CANCER, diabetes or several other diseases, may not be able to use this form of birth control. No one should ever 'borrow' a pill from a friend if they run out – two different types won't provide protection.

The pill gives absolutely no protection against SEXUALLY TRANSMITTED DISEASES such as HIV, the virus that can lead to AIDS. Anyone practising SAFER SEX should always use a CONDOM and a SPERMICIDE.

pimp

This is another word for a procurer, a man who 'owns' a PROSTITUTE in the sense that he finds clients for her (or makes her find her own) and makes his living from the money she earns. It's been used since the seventeenth century but no one really knows where the word comes from. It may come from the Old French word *pimpreneau* meaning 'scoundrel'. A female pimp is called a procuress or a MADAM if she runs a BROTHEL – but world-wide, pimping is generally seen to be a man's job. In the UK a pimp is commonly called a PONCE.

The legal term for pimping is 'living on IMMORAL earnings' and it is a criminal offence.

pin-up

In 1941 the American magazine *Life* carried an article which described the film star Dorothy Lamour as the 'No. 1 pin-up girl of the US Army'. A year later the editor of the GI's magazine called *Yank* sent a memo to his staff saying,

'Every issue should have a pin-up picture for soldiers to pin up on the barrack's wall to remind them of the girls back home.'

In the UK, the term pin-up girl has become obsolete and has been replaced by PAGE-THREE GIRL.

plating See FELLATIO.

platonic

If someone wants a platonic friendship, it means they want an intimate relationship but without any sex. This 'ideal' love gets its name from the ancient Greek philosopher Plato (427–347 BC) who wrote an essay about love, truth and moral goodness called *Symposium*.

playboy

This once meant a schoolboy actor, but early in the twentieth century it began to be used for a rich man with a showy lifestyle who was often seen in public with different women at expensive restaurants, nightclubs, casinos, etc. 'Playboy' is one of the few male-related terms that calls a man a boy (although a mature woman is often referred to as a girl).

In 1955 the American magazine *Playboy* began its long and successful life. An American dictionary of slang describes it as

'a popular man's magazine dealing with fashions, entertainment, etc. The term always implies wealth, education, social standing, and sophistication.'

This definition fails to point out that a 'playboy' is also sexually PROMISCUOUS. The main selling point of *Playboy* is its photos of naked female models, often posed to reveal their vagina; the magazine is little more than soft-core PORNOGRAPHY. The term 'centrefold' comes from the photo of a naked woman intended to sexually excite male readers which regularly appears in the two middle pages of *Playboy*. (See also PAGE-THREE GIRL and PIN-UP.) Hugh Hefner, the millionaire owner of *Playboy* magazine also ran a chain of clubs in which the 'hostesses' had to wear absurd 'bunny' costumes which emphasized their breasts and buttocks.

plonker

This word, very similar in sound and origin to BONK and bonker, emerged during the First World War (1914–1918) as British slang for SEXUAL INTERCOURSE and for PENIS. Since the 1950s it has also meant a CONDOM. Today it's often used as a derogatory (see Glossary) term for a useless or inadequate person, usually a man.

polygamy (pol-*lig*-gam-ee)

'Poly' is a prefix (see Glossary) from Greek meaning 'much, many'. 'Gamy' is from the Greek for marriage. Although 'polygamy' actually means having more than one wife or husband at the same time, it mostly refers only to the male custom of having more than one wife. The correct term for having more than one wife is 'polygyny' (gyny comes from the Greek for 'woman' – see QUEEN, while 'polyandry' means a woman who has one or more husbands (from the Greek word *andros* meaning 'a man').

During most of the five thousand years of recorded human history, male polygamy has been far more widespread than MONO-GAMY. In ancient Hebrew, Egyptian, Chinese and Babylonian times, men were permitted several wives. King Solomon, who ruled from about 955–935 BC was supposed to have had seven hundred of them – as well as three hundred CONCUBINES.

Polygamy survived among the early Hindus of India, at one time among Mormons and Anabaptists, and in Islam it is traditional but declining. A well-known exception to the Christian teaching against polygamy was Charlemagne, King of the Franks and Holy Roman Emperor (742–814), who had two wives, as did Philip of Hesse, another Holy Roman Emperor (1178–1208) and Frederick II of Prussia (1194–1250).

Polygamy is a crime in Western countries.

ponce

In the UK, this is slang for a PIMP. It first appeared in the early nineteenth century and may come from the phrase 'pounce on', perhaps because pimps pounce on destitute young women and bully them into becoming PROSTITUTES. Or it may be rhyming slang from the French Christian name, Alphonse.

Other slang terms include Charley or Joe Ronce, macaroni and mack man (both Black American slang), mac, mack, mackerel and mackerel-snapper (these terms may be a reference to the supposedly 'fishy' smell of unwashed female GENITALS; mackerel was slang for the MADAM of a BROTHEL as well as for a prostitute in the eighteenth century), player, fence and hoon (both Australian slang).

poof

Poof, poove, pouve, puff, pouffe and poofter are all terms which express contempt for a HOMOSEXUAL, mostly used by HETEROSEXUALS in the UK (see HOMOPHOBIA). Apart from 'poofter' which was first recorded in Australia in 1870, they all date back to the early 1930s. Puff, from cream or powder puff, meaning a weak or cowardly person is American slang for a GAY man.

poontang

Originally this was a highly sexist and racist term used by white Southern men in the USA for the VAGINA of a black woman, which dates back to the 1920s. It then came to mean a black woman viewed as a SEX OBJECT and a bit later it meant SEXUAL INTERCOURSE with a black woman. It may come from the French word *putain* meaning a cheap, low PROSTITUTE from the Creole (see Glossary) language of New Orleans. The term was later used by black men which might have made it less racist but makes it no less sexist.

It became a very common word among American GIs in the Vietnam war in the 1960s who commonly referred to any Vietnamese woman as 'poontang'.

popper

This is a slang term for the drug called Amyl Nitrate which comes in capsules which are called poppers because they have to be 'popped' open. The drug was designed to relieve heart attacks by enlarging the blood vessels and speeding up the heartbeat. It's inhaled and for a few minutes makes the heart pound and gives a. hot, flushed and dizzy feeling. Some people inhale a popper when they're having sex in order to intensify the sexual pleasure of an ORGASM. It's a very powerful drug and dangerous if taken often or by someone with a weak heart (and many people don't realize that they have a weak heart).

pornography

This comes from two Greek words, *porne* meaning WHORE and *graphos* meaning writing. In ancient Greece the *pornoi* were female slaves who worked in BROTHELS, the lowest rank of PROSTITUTES.

Until 'pornography' was coined (see Glossary) in the mid-nineteenth century, books with explicit descriptions of sex were usually referred to as BAWDY. At first, most of these types of book written in or translated into English were about whores and brothels – so a word meaning literally 'writing about prostitutes' was appropriate. But by the end of the eighteenth century the range of subject matter in books like these had widened considerably and anything that was impure, OBSCENE or EROTIC was called pornographic.

Pornography is generally reckoned to be different from erotic literature although both can make the reader sexually aroused. Pornography (or 'porn' as it's often shortened to) is widely used for erotic material (books, pictures, paintings, films, etc) with little or no literary or artistic merit and which degrades women. 'Soft-core' porn usually refers to magazines (see GLAMOUR, PLAYBOY) which show naked women, often quite romantically. 'Hard-core' porn is sexually explicit material which often shows violent sex (see MASOCHISM, SADISM).

post-coitum triste See ORGASM.

pox

Pox is an altered spelling of 'pocks', the plural of 'pock' which is a pustule or spot containing pus caused by a viral infection. In 1495 the French historian Jean Molinet was the first to record the name *les pocques* for the VENEREAL DISEASE which later came to be called SYPHILIS. One of the early symptoms of this SEXUALLY TRANSMITTED DISEASE is a small painless spot on the GENITALS. This was translated into English in the sixteenth century as 'the pox', sometimes 'the French pox' and has been the popular name for this disease ever since. At first 'pox' was Standard English but by the eighteenth century it was considered a vulgarism (see Glossary).

prat

In the sixteenth century a prat, or pratt, was slang for 'buttock'. By the seventeenth century it was criminal jargon, or cant (see Glossary), for a tinderbox, a metal box containing everything needed to light a fire. It may be the association with 'the fires of love' that gave 'prat' the sense of CUNT in the nineteenth century. 'Prat' is used interchangeably with 'TWAT' in the UK, for someone who is a bit stupid.

pregnancy

'Pre' means 'before', while the last part of the word comes from the Latin for 'to be born'. Pregnancy lasts from CONCEPTION (when an OVUM is FERTILIZED by a SPERM) until labour. On average it lasts for thirty-eight weeks unless it is ended by a MISCARRIAGE, an ABORTION, or if the baby is born prematurely. Because the exact moment of conception is uncertain, pregnancy is usually dated from the first day of the last PERIOD which is likely to be a fortnight before conception, making a total of forty weeks.

It's only fairly recently that pregnancy has become something women aren't ashamed to reveal to the rest of the world. A hundred years ago it was not the done thing to either show it or talk about it – perhaps because it implied that a pregnant woman must have had SEXUAL INTERCOURSE which wasn't considered very 'ladylike'. This may explain why there are so many euphemisms (see Glossary) which allowed people to talk about pregnancy in a roundabout way. Queen Victoria used '*enciente*' (French for 'pregnant') even to her own female children.

Other terms include expectant or expecting, a bun in the oven, in the family way, gone, in a delicate condition, fallen, on the hill, preggers, puffed, pumped, that way, wearing her apron high, with child, in the club, knocked up, pudding club, up the duff, clucky (Australian), on the nest, up the spout or up the pole. 'With child' has been used since at least 1175.

pregnancy advisory services

See under Pregnancy Services in the Yellow Pages for organisations that can provide testing, counselling and practical support. Some of these organisations may be opposed to ABORTION.

premarital sex

The formal term for 'sex before marriage'.

premature ejaculation

This is the name given if a boy or man COMES, or EJACULATES, before his PENIS has entered his partner's VAGINA or before he is ready for it. It can leave him and his partner feeling rather frustrated. It happens to most males at some time or other during their lives, and most often when they have SEXUAL INTERCOURSE for the very first time or for the first time with a new partner. It's usually just a case of first-time nerves.

premenstrual syndrome (PMS) or tension (PMT)

Many girls and women feel irritable, depressed, bloated, headachey and have sore or tender breasts around the time their PERIOD is due to start. Some doctors believe it is due to a lack of the HORMONE called PROGESTERONE which in extreme and rare cases can cause a woman to act irrationally or violently.

Any girl who suffers from PMS should consult her doctor, who may prescribe progesterone injections which some find helpful. The symptoms may also be relieved by taking vitamin B6 or a herbal remedy called Evening Primrose Oil, both of which can be obtained at the chemist.

prepuce (pree-pyoohs)
In females this is the technical term for the fold of tissue at the point where the inner lips, or LABIA, join and protect the CLITORIS. In males it is the FORESKIN.

priapism (pry-*ap*-ism)
This is a rare and extremely painful condition in which the PENIS stays ERECT without the boy or man having any feelings of sexual DESIRE or excitement. It gets its name from an ancient Greek myth. Priapus was the son of two notoriously PROMISCUOUS parents, Aphrodite, the goddess of beauty and love (see APHRODISIAC) and Dionysus, the god of fertility, vegetation and wine. Priapus was an ugly child with an enormous penis which the goddess, Hera, had given him because she disapproved of his mother's sexual conquests. Not that the size of his GENITALS did him much good. When he was drunk Priapus tried to RAPE the CHASTE goddess, Hestia, while she was asleep; but an ass started to bray and woke her up. Her screams scared him so much that he ran away, looking more foolish than the ass.

The size of a penis makes no difference to the amount of sexual pleasure a boy or man can give or receive – and drunkenness is not a recipe for sexual success (see BREWER'S DROOP).

prick
In the late sixteenth century, this was Standard English for PENIS. By 1700 it had become a vulgarism and in the twentieth century it was what language experts call a 'low colloquialism'. (See Glossary for all these language terms.) Prick is one of several slang terms for the penis which have a connection with making a hole, presumably a reference to the HYMEN, the piece of skin tissue which, in some girls who are VIRGINS, covers the entrance to the VAGINA. Other similar terms include bayonet, cherry-splitter, dagger, pecker, poker, prong, ramrod, and rod.

The phrase 'you silly prick' is a mildly contemptuous term usually applied to boys and men, meaning a fairly stupid person. For pricktease, see COCKTEASE.

procreate (pro-kree-ate)
This is a formal word used for the act of creating a baby.

progesterone (pro-*jest*-er-one) See HORMONE and CORPUS LUTEUM.

progestogen (pro-*jest*-o-jen)
This is a natural or synthetic substance that acts like the female HORMONE called progesterone.

promiscuity (prom-isk-yoo-itty)
From the Latin for 'indiscriminate', this means having several or many different sexual partners. Although promiscuity seems to be more acceptable for men than for women in our society, it's widely frowned upon by those who believe that sex should be saved for marriage. It also has health risks. Promiscuity in itself doesn't cause a SEXUALLY TRANSMITTED DISEASE, but each time you have sex with a different person you are increasing the chance of coming across someone who is infected. For some people SAFER SEX means sticking to just one partner.

prophylactic
From a Greek word meaning 'to keep guard before', in medical terminology a 'prophylactic medicine' prevents an illness. In the USA, CONDOMS are sometimes called preventives or prophylactics, often shortened to 'pro'. (In the UK, a 'pro' is more likely to mean a PROSTITUTE.)

prostate
One of the internal male sex organs, the prostate is a mass of muscle fibres and small glands about the size and shape of a chestnut, which lies just in front of the place where the URETHRA connects to the

bladder. The word comes from the Greek for 'placed before'. It produces a milky-looking alkaline fluid forming the SEMEN, which protects the SPERM from the acidic environment of the URETHRA and the VAGINA.

In middle and old age the prostate gland in some men becomes enlarged making it either difficult or painful to pee or making him want to pee frequently. An operation to remove it, called a prostatectomy, relieves these symptoms. Although it usually makes a man STERILE because he can no longer produce semen, his ERECTION and ORGASM will not be affected.

prostitute

The origins of this word lie in the Latin *pro* meaning 'before' and *statuere* meaning 'to set up', or 'place'. These form a word with the sense of 'to set up in front of everyone'. The meaning developed from this, firstly to 'expose publicly' and 'offer for sale' and eventually to 'make available for sex in return for money'.

When the word first entered the English language in the sixteenth century it had the sense of 'to offer with complete devotion' as well as 'to offer oneself to unlawful SEXUAL INTERCOURSE, usually for hire.' By the mid-seventeenth century 'prostitute', meaning a woman who sells her sexual services, more or less replaced older words like BAWD, HARLOT, WHORE and strumpet.

Past and present slang terms include ASS pedlar, bat, CALL-GIRL, cat, commercial BEAVER, dirtyleg, *fille de joie* (French for 'girl of joy'), flatback (see MISSIONARY POSITION), floozy, HOOKER, lady of the evening, pross, puta, putana (from the French *putain* meaning 'whore'), quiff, Sadie (this may be connected with SADISM), sidewalk susie, skank, skeezer, TAIL pedlar, working broad, and working girl.

Apart from 'call boy', 'male model', 'RENT-BOY' and perhaps GIGOLO there aren't many words for a HETEROSEXUAL male prostitute.

prurient

From the Latin for 'itch, long for, be WANTON', this word first meant 'having itching DESIRE' and later came to mean 'given to LEWD thoughts' or 'showing an unhealthy interest in sexual matters'. It's often used to describe the way in which tabloid newspapers, while claiming to be morally offended by certain sexual behaviour, aim to TITILLATE readers by giving graphic and lurid detail.

puberty (*pyoo*-ber-tee)

From the Latin word for 'adult', this is the stage of development at the age of about eleven to thirteen in girls and twelve to fourteen in boys, when our bodies start to produce HORMONES which make our secondary sex characteristics start to appear.

In girls, these are BREASTS, a more rounded body, underarm and PUBIC HAIR and the size and colour of the VULVA. In boys, they are voice-breaking, PENIS growth, and pubic, facial and body hair. A girl knows she has reached puberty when she has her first PERIOD (see MENARCHE) and a boy usually knows when he has his first EJACULATION, sometimes when he has a WET DREAM.

Until the hormones settle down to a regular rate of production, many young people feel a bit unsettled. Puberty is a time when we start taking an interest in sex – either with the opposite sex (see HETEROSEXUAL) or with someone of the same sex (see CRUSH, HOMOSEXUAL). But although girls' bodies could technically produce a child, emotionally they don't feel anywhere near ready for it. Puberty is followed by ADOLESCENCE.

A 'puberty rite' is a term for a ritual or ceremony practised in various societies in which the GENITALS (usually of males) may be pierced or scarred.

pubes (pyoobz)

Coming from a Latin word meaning 'manhood', 'body hair' and 'pubic region', this is an informal term for the female and male pubic area and for PUBIC HAIR.

pubic hair

When we reach PUBERTY, pubic hair starts to grow on the MONS VENERIS and around the outer lips (the LABIA majora) of girls and at the base of the PENIS and on and around the TESTICLES of boys. It is fairly fine hair at first and later becomes more coarse. It's usually darker than the hair that grows on the head of white or pale-skinned people – if it's the same colour it sometimes gets called 'cuffs and collars'. Other slang terms include beard, BEAVER, brillo (a brand of wire wool pot-scourers) brush, bush, cotton, Fort Bushy, garden, grass, lawn, muff, squirrel, wool, wire wool.

pubic lice See CRABS.

pudendum (pyoo-*den*-dum)
This is Latin for VULVA meaning 'something to be ashamed of'. Until the sixteenth century the Standard English term (see Glossary) was CUNT, but once this became unacceptable in polite society it was replaced by 'pudendum'. The plural is pudenda.

pulling out See COITUS INTERRUPTUS.

pussy
Puss or pussy have been used as slang terms for the female PUDENDUM since the seventeenth century. In the nineteenth century they began to be used as a child's pet name for a cat. A cat's fur presumably reminds people of pubic hair – both feel nice to stroke – but how children picked up what was considered to be a rather rude word remains a mystery. In the twentieth century 'pussy' became a general word for a woman, especially one thought of by men as a SEX OBJECT.

Pygmalionism
A psychologist uses this term for someone who falls in love with a person or object of their own creation. Its name comes from the ancient Greek myth about Pygmalion, who fell in love with the goddess Aphrodite (see APHRODISIAC). Because she refused to make love with him he carved an ivory statue of her and put it in his bed. Aphrodite took pity on him and brought this image of herself to life as Galatea, who bore him two children. The English writer George Bernard Shaw updated this myth in his play *Pygmalion*, which was later turned into a musical and a film called *My Fair Lady*.

Q

queen

Originating in an Indo-European root word (see Glossary) from which the Greek word *gune*, meaning woman, developed, this gave the English language such words as gynaecology, ANDROGYNY, misogyny (hatred of women) and various other woman-related words that have 'gyny' or 'gyne' in them. It also produced two Old English words, *cwen*, meaning 'female ruler or wife of a King' and *cwene*, meaning 'woman'. It is from these two words that we get the modern word 'queen' and an older word, quean, which meant woman (and still does in Scottish dialect).

Interestingly, during the reign of Queen Victoria (1819–1901) 'queen' began to be used in a negative sexual way. At first it was slang for 'girlfriend' and later came to mean PROSTITUTE. In Scotland, 'Quean' went through the same process 300 years earlier.

In 1920s Australia, 'queen' became slang for an EFFEMINATE man and a male HOMOSEXUAL, a sense it once had in England in the early seventeenth century to describe King James who was a well-known PAEDOPHILE. It was used by HETEROSEXUALS as a term of abuse (see HOMOPHOBIA) in the same way that other woman-words have been used to put down GAYS (see PANSY). In the 1960s, 'queen' was adopted by homosexuals in the USA in much the same way as they adopted 'gay' for their own use. It tends to be used in terms like drag queen, RUBBER queen, RIM queen, etc to describe the sort of sexual activity preferred by a gay man.

queer

Possibly from a German word meaning 'crooked, perverse', the standard meaning of 'queer' is 'something that differs in some odd way from what is usual or normal'. As slang, it has a long history with many different senses. It once meant the opposite of 'rum' meaning 'excellent', but later came to mean 'criminal or counterfeit'. In the early sixteenth century, 'queer' appeared with the sense of 'odd, eccentric' in Scottish dialect. A hundred years later 'to queer' someone meant to cheat or hoax them. In Victorian times, it gained the sense 'drunk' and later 'unwell, giddy'. This influenced yet another sense of 'strange behaviour, madness'. In the twentieth century 'queer' came to mean HOMOSEXUAL in the USA. It was used of both LESBIANS and GAY men and it became a fairly polite word among HETEROSEXUALS.

Many gays object to the term queer, perhaps because with all its other senses the word implies that to be gay isn't just to be different, but also somehow criminal or mad. 'Queer-bashing', the beating-up of gays by HOMOPHOBES, is widely used by STRAIGHTS and gays alike. In the 1990s, some lesbians and gay men began to reclaim the word 'queer' with the slogan, 'We're here, and we're queer'.

quim

This has been slang for the VAGINA since the seventeenth century. It may come from the Spanish word meaning 'to burn' which could be a reference to the painful scorching feeling that men get in their PENIS when they have SYPHILIS. (See PRAT for another connection between the vagina and fire.) Another theory is that it may come from the Welsh word *cwm* meaning cleft or valley.

In the nineteenth century the vagina was sometimes called a quim-box and female PUBIC HAIR was known as a quim-bush, quim-whiskers and a quim-wig (see MERKIN). The penis was a quim-stake or quim-wedge and a man who went with PROSTITUTES was a quim-sticker. Quim-sticking, quim-wedging or quimming all meant SEXUAL INTERCOURSE. None of these terms is used today, although quim itself is beginning to reappear in the UK and has been reclaimed by some lesbian feminists as the title of a magazine.

R

rag

'On the rag', a term for a PERIOD, is a reference to a SANITARY
TOWEL. Before the days of disposable sanitary protection, women
used to wear cloths or rags which they washed out and used again.
In some countries women still have to do this – either because
they're poor or because politicians and manufacturers don't think it
necessary to ensure women can get cheap, hygienic and convenient
protection.

The Rastafarian word 'rasclat' meaning 'blood cloth' is a term of
abuse hurled at people who are very strongly disliked. Language like
this doesn't help to make girls and women feel very good about
themselves when they're having their periods.

randy

In the eighteenth century, if you felt randy you were feeling violent
as well as sexually aroused and LECHEROUS. The word may come
from an old use of 'rand' meaning 'to rave' or perhaps from the
Hindu word *randi-baz* meaning 'lecher'. In the twentieth century the
sense of violence disappeared from its meaning and by the 1960s it
was an almost respectable term to describe someone who either felt
sexually excited or was always wanting to have sex.

Other slang terms with a similar meaning include antsy, goatish,
hot, hot as a three-dollar pistol, hot to trot, horny, hunky, itching,
rammy, rooty (see ROOT), sexy, steamed on.

rape

To be raped means being forced to have SEXUAL INTERCOURSE
against your will. It is a serious crime which often goes unreported
and unconvicted for two main reasons. The first is that the law in

most places defines rape as the forced PENETRATION of the PENIS into the VAGINA or ANUS. This means that unless the rapist EJACULATES and there is actual evidence of SEMEN, penetration can be difficult to prove. The forced penetration of another object – rape victims report the use of broken bottles, knives, sticks and other weapons – does not count. Forced ORAL SEX is also excluded. In New York, however, rape is legally defined as the forced penetration of the penis or any object by a person of either sex into the vagina or any orifice of another, whatever the relationship with the victim.

The other reason why women often don't report rape and why there is such a low conviction rate of rapists, is the widely-held view that a girl or woman can't be raped because she secretly wants it, was 'asking for it' or enjoyed being treated roughly. Behind these myths lie the idea that when a woman says 'no' she really means 'yes', and that all females are silly creatures forever changing their minds. A further myth suggests that some women 'deserve' to be raped because of the clothes they wear or because of how they behave. This sort of attitude means that when the rape victim is giving evidence in court (as a witness for the prosecution) she or he is made to feel as if they are the guilty person.

These myths may spring from a confusion between a rape fantasy and the reality of rape. This confusion can be seen from the history of the meaning of the word. Over the years, the words rape, rapt, rapture, ravage, ravish and ravishing, which all come from the same Latin word, have all meant 'forced sexual violation' and 'to be carried to a state of ecstasy and delight'. However, the point about a rape fantasy is that you have the power to choose the time, the place, the so-called rapist, and when to end it. In reality you are powerless. A rape fantasy is usually about being SEDUCED and wanted. Rape itself is about hatred.

Anyone who has been raped knows that rape is so horrific that no one would ever ask for it, secretly desire or enjoy it in real life. It is a deeply traumatic experience to have someone – whether they are a stranger, an acquaintance, lover or husband – force sex upon you against your will. More teenagers are raped by someone they know than by a stranger – known as date or acquaintance rape. The rapist uses the threat of physical violence and/or of moral blackmail to get their way.

No one ever 'deserves' to be raped. A girl or boy wearing apparently seductive clothes, who acts in a sexy manner, or who walks alone at night may be asking for a good time or is just trying to get home – but that's all. Given the widespread belief in the myths and the high incidence of the crime, you might think them foolish – but mere foolishness does not deserve to be punished as severely as by being raped. Any ideas of ecstasy or delight cannot be those of the victim who is treated not as a person who is valued, loved and cared for, but as an object, a thing with a vagina or anus.

For professional help and advice if you are raped, see COUNSEL-LING.

red light

This is an American term for a district where PROSTITUTES live and/or work. It comes from the nineteenth century term 'red light house', for a BROTHEL which once hung a red lamp outside.

rent boy

In the 1890s 'rent' was slang for a male HOMOSEXUAL PROSTITUTE. In the 1920s it became slang for blackmail – presumably because male homosexuality was illegal and some 'rent' would threaten to expose their clients unless they paid up. The term 'rent boy' is a 1960s term for a young male prostitute who offers his services to older male homosexuals (see PEDERAST). In many countries the AGE OF CONSENT is higher for GAYS than for HETEROSEXUALS, so a 'boy' may be as old as twenty.

rhythm method

Also known as the safe period method, this is a very unreliable form of birth control based on the assumption that every girl's or woman's MENSTRUAL cycle is absolutely regular. By taking careful notes about the various phases of her cycle, she may be able to roughly predict when she will ovulate. This happens about fourteen days before the start of her next PERIOD. If no SEXUAL INTERCOURSE takes place during the three or four days before and after OVULATION – the so-called 'unsafe' time to have sex – it's unlikely that she will become PREGNANT. The method may be made a bit more reliable by keeping a temperature chart and using a specially-made thermometer (most women have a very slight rise in temperature immediately after they ovulate).

It's virtually impossible to predict exactly when ovulation will take place. Very few girls or women have absolutely regular periods and ovulation can happen earlier or later than usual due to excitement, depression or illness. This method should only be used by couples who don't mind if they have a baby. It's the only method of CONTRACEPTION permitted by the Roman Catholic Church, which is why it's sometimes referred to as 'Vatican roulette'.

ride

Horses provided a rich source for slang words and terms connected with sex. The basic image is of a wild mare which is tamed, domesticated and made to work for men.

'To ride' has been used to describe the action of having SEXUAL INTERCOURSE with a woman since the Middle Ages. By the late sixteenth century men spoke of 'mounting' a woman when talking in rather crude terms about COPULATION. A harridan (which now means a cross-tempered old woman) came from a French word meaning a tired old horse, and was defined by the famous dictionary writer Samuel Johnson as 'a decayed strumpet' (a strumpet was slang for WHORE). In the eighteenth century, 'a hack' (also from the French) meaning a slow horse, was slang for a PROSTITUTE. A jade, now obsolete (see Glossary), was a worn-out old horse in the fourteenth century and, according to Samuel Johnson's 1755 dictionary, 'A sorry woman. A word of contempt noting sometimes age, but generally VICE'. 'Rider' has meant a RANDY man since the eighteenth century.

When applied to women, most of these horsey terms suggest male contempt. The same is not true for men. Stud, an Anglo-Irish term shortened from 'studstallion', has been a positive term meaning a sexy or virile man since the 1920s.

right to life

This is the slogan of people who are against ABORTION and who take the view that life exists from the moment of CONCEPTION. They are opposed by people who are 'pro-choice', who believe it does not make sense to refer to an EMBRYO or FOETUS as a living person until it reaches the stage at around twenty-six weeks when, if it was born, it could survive.

rimming

In the nineteenth century, 'to rim' was British slang for ANAL INTERCOURSE; in the twentieth century it became American slang for sucking the ANUS, which is now mainly used by GAY men. Rimming (occasionally reaming) means licking or sucking the anus or lubricating the anus with saliva, the formal term for which is anilingus. It is not a SAFER SEX practice since it involves coming into contact with body fluids which may carry HIV or the HEPATITIS B virus.

risqué (*riss*-kay)

The Victorians borrowed this word directly from the French for 'to risk'. In English it means an INDECENT or slightly OBSCENE remark.

root

Since the nineteenth century this has been slang for the PENIS, usually with an ERECTION. It probably comes from an image of a man firmly implanted inside a woman during SEXUAL INTERCOURSE or a stiff penis sticking up and growing like a tree. This would explain why the verb 'to root' became slang for COPULATION. 'Rooting' is the slang most commonly used in Australia for MAKING LOVE; 'a root' is a rather crude term for a sexual partner suggesting that this is all there is to say about them. To be 'rooty' means the same as RANDY, and may come from 'rut' (from the Latin for 'to roar'), which is a word used to describe the state of sexual readiness in animals, especially deer, when the female is on heat.

rough trade

Among PROSTITUTES this is slang for a client (see also JOHN). Among

HETEROSEXUALS (sometimes 'a bit of rough') it means a sexual partner who is working-class. In HOMOSEXUAL slang it means a tough or SADISTIC gay man, one who prefers ANAL INTERCOURSE in order to hurt his partner, or a male prostitute who agrees to be subjected to this sort of treatment by his 'trade'.

RU 486

The chemical name for this HORMONE drug is mifepristone. It was first developed as a medical treatment to bring about an ABORTION but is now also used as a morning-after pill for girls and women who have had unprotected SEXUAL INTERCOURSE and fear they might be pregnant. If used as EMERGENCY CONTRACEPTION it must be taken within three days (72 hours) after sex has taken place. It is less likely to make you feel sick or make you vomit and appears to be more effective in preventing pregnancy than other morning-after pills. But because no one really knows the effects of using this drug often (it's feared it may cause blood-clotting in the veins and arteries), it shouldn't be used repeatedly.

rub

Since the sixteenth century 'to rub up' has meant to stroke or lovingly caress someone to make them feel sexually AROUSED. By the seventeeth century 'to rub up' or 'rub off' meant either to have SEXUAL INTERCOURSE or to MASTURBATE. Before the word LESBIAN came to be used for a female HOMOSEXUAL in the 1890s, the words 'fricatrice' and 'tribade' were both used. They come from the Latin and Greek verbs meaning 'to rub'.

rubber

In sexual terms rubber has a couple of senses. Since the 1930s it's been slang for a CONDOM, because they're made of rubber latex. Rubber is also a fairly common sexual FETISH – there are people who get turned on, or who can only get turned on, if they or their partner wears shiny rubber clothes. A male GAY who is into rubber is known as a rubber QUEEN. Psychologists think this fetish may be triggered by early childhood experiences with rubber pants worn over nappies or rubber sheets used to protect the mattress from bed-wetting. It's not such a strange fetish since other shiny clothes, made of silk or satin for example, make many people feel sexy.

S

sadism (*say*-dizm)

This sexual PERVERSION involving the domination and infliction of pain and humiliation on a sexual partner, gets its name from the Marquis de Sade (1740–1814), the French writer who spent much of his life in prison and mental asylums for crimes of DEBAUCHERY. His most famous novels, *Justine* and *One Hundred and Twenty Days of Sodom* (see SODOMY), contain graphic accounts of sexual acts, many of which are highly perverse. Some people think his novels are classic works of literary value which reflect de Sade's belief that both women and men should have total freedom in all matters. Others find them OBSCENE and PORNOGRAPHIC. It's now thought that de Sade never committed any of the crimes of which he was accused and that his writings merely reflect a vivid imagination involving a lot of sexual FANTASY.

A person who enjoys being treated sadistically is a MASOCHIST. When both are mixed together it's known as SADO-MASOCHISM.

sado-masochism (S & M) (say-doh-*mass*-ock-izm)

SADISM and MASOCHISM are psycho-sexual disorders involving pain and humiliation. The combination of both is called sado-masochism, often shortened to S & M, which is sometimes interpreted to stand for Submission and Mastery.

A sado-masochistic relationship can be mutually satisfying and exciting if one person (the sadist) gets sexual pleasure and sexual satisfaction from inflicting pain on his/her partner while the other (the masochist) gets sexual pleasure and satisfaction from being hurt. To a certain extent many sexual relationships involve a degree of pain – a LOVE-BITE is an example of the sort of pain that some people enjoy. It's an ABUSE, however, if someone forces their partner to suffer pain against their will. If a person can't get sexually aroused unless they dominate and cause their partner pain or unless they are totally dominated and hurt, S & M is said to be a sexual PERVERSION.

safe period See RHYTHM METHOD.

safer sex
The term 'safer sex' was coined in the 1980s to educate people about ways of enjoying sex without running too great a risk of getting HIV. Everyone has to get involved – AIDS isn't something that only GAY men have to think about. You can't tell simply by looking at someone whether they are infected with HIV – they may not even know themselves. Safer sex is about preventing any body fluids getting to a part of the body where the virus could be absorbed into your or your partner's bloodstream. And it's also about making love and caring.

SEXUAL INTERCOURSE (vaginal and anal) without the protection of a CONDOM is the riskiest form of sex in which either partner, if they're infected, could pass on the virus. The risk is greatly reduced if you use a CONDOM with a SPERMICIDE. The spermicide is very important because condoms can split or have tiny holes in them. It also kills the virus on contact, as well as the sperm. A LUBRICANT should also be used since it helps the PENIS slide in and out more smoothly and helps prevent the condom from splitting. This is especially important for couples having anal sex, who should also use thicker condoms for this purpose.

ORAL SEX, when you lick or suck your partner's penis or vagina, is a low-risk activity because, even if the male comes inside his partner's mouth the virus will probably be destroyed by saliva and stomach juices. Any cuts or sores in the mouth may increase the risk. So may CUNNILINGUS during a woman's period. To be really safe in all forms of oral sex, many couples use a condom or place a DENTAL DAM over the vagina. It is highly unlikely that a deep FRENCH KISS could put either partner at risk.

Sex doesn't have to involve PENETRATION and there are literally many ways of making love, of having an orgasm and of letting someone know you care without running any risk at all. Kissing, stroking, licking, sucking, rubbing, touching, massaging, whispering, laughing and talking all turn most people on. Massage oil or even baby lotion feels wonder fully sensuous. Finding out where your partner likes to be touched (see EROGENOUS ZONES) gives a lot of pleasure and sexual excitement, as does mutual MASTURBATION. It's perfectly safe to COME on each other's skin as long as you cover up any cuts or sores.

sanitary towel or napkin

These are pads of cotton, usually with a plastic lining on the outside, which are worn inside the underpants to absorb the MENSTRUAL bleeding of a PERIOD. They come in different sizes and thicknesses; some can be stuck to the pants to make sure they don't move about, others have loops at either end to fix to a couple of hooks on a belt which is worn around the waist inside the clothes. There's no reason why they should show even under quite tight-fitting trousers. Those who find them a bit bulky may prefer to use TAMPONS which fit inside the VAGINA.

Sappho

The poet Sappho lived on the Greek island of Lesbos around 600 BC. Plato admired her poetry so much he called her the 'tenth muse' and today she is regarded as one of the greatest of the ancient poets. Sadly, very little of her poetry survives. The fragments that have been found reveal the love she felt for other women. Sapphism was one of the words used for a female HOMOSEXUAL until the nineteenth century when 'LESBIAN' was coined (see Glossary). Other words were 'fricatrice' and 'tribade' (see RUB).

It seems clear from Sappho's writing that lesbianism was acceptable at the time she lived but subsequent societies, especially Christian society, condemned it (see HOMOPHOBIA). Perhaps because later generations couldn't accept that so great a poet was a lesbian, a myth was invented claiming Sappho killed herself by plunging into the sea because a man named Phaon didn't return her love.

It is difficult to show the depth of feeling, passion and beauty of

Sappho's writing in just one short extract of the existing fragments, but something of her brilliance shines through in this verse:

> Some an army of horsemen, some an army on foot
> and some say a fleet of ships is the loveliest sight
> on this dark earth; but I say it is whatever you desire:

satyriasis

In ancient Greek and Roman times, the satyrs were half-men, half-goats who attended Dionysius or Bacchus (gods of fertility and wine) and were well-known for their wild sexual ORGIES. To call a man a satyr is to suggest that he's highly-sexed and PROMISCUOUS.

Satyriasis (also known as DON JUAN syndrome) is the term for a male psycho-sexual disorder involving an obsessive desire for sexual gratification that's never satisfied. Psychologists believe that it comes from deeply-embedded emotional needs such as the need to compensate for failures in other areas of life, or an attempt to deny HOMOSEXUAL tendencies. See also NYMPHOMANIA.

scarlet woman

This term for a sexually PROMISCUOUS woman, a painted JEZEBEL, a WHORE or adulteress (see ADULTERY) comes from the Book of Revelations in the New Testament where St John describes a vision of a woman sitting 'upon a scarlet coloured beast, full of names of blasphemy, having seven heads and ten horns'. She was dressed in scarlet and purple and in her hand was a golden cup 'full of abominations and filthiness of her fornication'. (See FORNICATE.) On her forehead was written 'Mystery, Babylon the Great, The Mother of Harlots and Abominations of The Earth'. St John was actually referring to the city of Rome where Christians were being persecuted.

In the sixteenth century the early puritan settlers in New England used to sew a scarlet 'A' for 'adulteress' on the dress of a guilty woman as American writer Nathaniel Hawthorne (1804–1864) describes in his famous novel *The Scarlet Letter*:

'She turned her eyes downwards at the scarlet letter, and even touched it with her finger, to assure herself that the infant and the shame was real.'

scatology

From the Greek word for FAECES, this is the study or interest in excrement, filth, and OBSCENITY. People who like using 'dirty' words, especially those connected to shitting and to ANAL SEX during sexual encounters are said to use scatological language. Taken to extremes it becomes a PERVERSION.

schmuck

In the nineteenth century, the German word '*schmuck*', meaning 'jewel, ornament', was adopted by European Yiddish-speaking Jews as a euphemism (see Glossary) for the female PUDENDA. (In English, 'jewel-box' has been a coy euphemism for the VAGINA since the eighteenth century.) By 1910 Yiddish-speaking Jews in the USA were using 'schmuck' to mean 'fool'. To call someone a schmuck is the same as saying, 'You silly CUNT!'

screw

The word 'screw' probably originates from the Latin for 'breeding sow.' The connection will be obvious to anyone who's seen the spirally-ridged shape of a hog's erect PENIS.

By the seventeenth century, 'screw' was a verb meaning 'to PENETRATE with a winding course'. Within a hundred years it was coarse slang for 'to COPULATE with a woman' and a vulgar term for a common PROSTITUTE. Finally, the word was used for any woman seen as a SEX OBJECT. Today it's used as slang for SEXUAL INTER-COURSE by both women and men, although many women object to it because it makes sex sound as if it's something that men do *to* women rather than *with* them.

scrotum/scrotal sac (*skro*-tum)

In Latin a *scrotum* is a sheath for arrows made of animal hide. The word entered the English language in the sixteenth century meaning the pouch of skin containing the male TESTICLES, EPIDIDYMIS and VAS DEFERENS in which SPERM are produced and stored. The scrotum is placed at the base of the penis with the left side normally lower than the right.

scrubber

Today, a scrubber is a slang term for a coarse or vulgar sexually PROMISCUOUS woman. It originally meant a tough plant or a bush (also called a shrub) and later developed the sense of 'a poorly-dressed fellow'. Perhaps because domestic servants used brushes made from scrub and tended to be poor and badly-dressed due to low wages, 'scrubber' came to be used in the sixteenth century for someone (usually a female) who cleaned, or scrubbed floors. The sense of sexual promiscuity may have come about because many scrubbers had to become PROSTITUTES to earn enough money to survive.

In Australia, scrubber has a slightly different history. In the mid-nineteenth century 'a scrub' was an animal or person who lived in the bush. By the 1970s 'scrubber' meant a woman who was like 'a mare that runs wild in the scrub country, COPULATING indiscriminately with stray stallions'.

scumbag

This is slang for a CONDOM and for someone who is disgusting and filthy both physically and morally. In Standard English 'scum', from an Old German word meaning foam, means the pollutants or impurities that float on the surface of a liquid. Bag (meaning a loose container) has been slang for a disliked and/or filthy old woman since Victorian times when it also meant a part-time female PROSTITUTE. Not surprisingly, given that 'scum' is also a slang term for SEMEN, a scumbag was once slang for an old or diseased prostitute.

seduce/seduction

From the Latin for 'to lead away', if you seduce someone, you incite them to disobedience or disloyalty or you lead them astray from moral principles, especially by persuasion or false promises. Seduction is used in a sexual sense to mean enticing someone, especially a female VIRGIN, to have SEXUAL INTERCOURSE by using guile and flattery. A seductive person is someone who has alluring or charming qualities and uses them to entice his or her 'victim'. Seduction and RAPE are therefore different in that being seduced can be pleasurable and something that is finally agreed to, but rape is totally against the victim's will. Rape is a crime, seduction is not. This may explain why many rapists try to convince the courts that their victim was 'only playing hard to get' and was seduced rather than raped.

seed

This is a biblical word for SPERM. If a boy or man 'plants his seed', it means he has SEXUAL INTERCOURSE usually for purposes of PROCREATION rather than pleasure. A young man is sometimes described as 'sewing his wild oats', which means he is sexually PROMISCUOUS until he 'settles down' with one partner.

self-abuse See MASTURBATION.

semen (*see*-men)

Based on a Latin word meaning 'sew' this is the thick, sticky, whitish fluid containing SPERM that is ejaculated by the male when he reaches ORGASM. The average amount of semen produced by a healthy, fertile male contains between 100 and 120 million sperm, weighs about four grams (roughly a couple of small spoonfuls), is non-poisonous, and contains less than thirty-five calories mainly in proteins and fats.

Semen is one of the body fluids which, in a person with HIV infection, carries the virus that can lead to AIDS. This is why a CONDOM should always be used during SEXUAL INTERCOURSE (see SAFER SEX).

Slang terms include come, cream, cum, gism, goo, hockey, jam, JISM, jizz, juice, load, love juice, man oil, scum (see SCUMBAG), SPUNK, water of life and whipped cream.

seminal duct

This is the popular term for the VAS DEFERENS, which are two tubes in the male internal reproductive system that carry SPERM from the EPIDIDYMIS (inside the SCROTUM) to the PROSTATE gland. It is these ducts that are cut during a VASECTOMY.

seminal vesicle (*vess*-ikl)

Every male has two of these small tubes attached to the PROSTATE gland. They secrete a fluid which helps protect the SPERM when they reach the somewhat alkaline environment of the VAGINA. Vesicle comes from a Latin word meaning 'small sac containing fluid'.

sensual/sensuous

Something that suggests a liking for sexual pleasures is described as sensual. Similar words are voluptuous and sultry. Something that gives EROTIC pleasure through one of the five senses is called sensuous. For example, velvet or silk can feel sensuous; a piece of music can sound sensuous.

sex object

This early 1960s term means someone who is treated not as a whole person but simply as an object which has no purpose other than to provide sexual satisfaction. Many girls and women feel that this is how they are regarded by boys and men who refer to them as a CUNT or any of the other terms used by male CHAUVINISTS, who WOLF-WHISTLE, or who sexually HARASS them.

sex symbol

A symbol, from the Greek word meaning 'token' or 'mark', is a shape, design, or idea that is used to represent something. A sex symbol is usually a famous woman or man who many people have FANTASIES about having sex with. Sex symbols come and go – a pop star may find her or himself a sex symbol one year and completely forgotten the next. Marilyn Monroe is probably the most famous sex symbol of the twentieth century for males (see also PIN-UP); Rudolf Valentino was a hugely popular sexual fantasy figure for females.

sexism

This means discriminating against someone simply because of their GENDER. Because we live in a society where men as a whole have more power than most women, a sexist usually means a boy or man who treats girls and women not just differently but less well than they treat other males. Although the word itself wasn't coined (see Glossary) until 1965, the discrimination against women by men has gone on for centuries. See also CHAUVINIST.

sexual intercourse

Intercourse, from the Latin word meaning 'act of running between' means a connection between people or, in a slightly different sense, an exchange, especially of thoughts or feelings. Social intercourse means talking and relating to at least one other person. Sexual intercourse is usually used to mean the HETEROSEXUAL 'sex act' involving PENETRATION of the VAGINA by the PENIS. Anal intercourse is penetration of the ANUS (see ANAL SEX). Oral intercourse is penetration of the mouth by the penis (see ORAL SEX).

The formal terms for sexual intercourse (usually shortened to 'intercourse') are COITUS and COPULATION. The best known informal or slang terms are 'to MAKE LOVE' and 'to FUCK'.

Intercourse is most pleasurable when it starts with FOREPLAY, making both partners feel sexually excited. For a girl or woman this means the lips, or LABIA, of her vagina become slightly swollen and her CLITORIS becomes ERECT and pokes out of its little hood, making it easier to be stimulated. Her vagina may produce a natural juice, or LUBRICANT. As a boy or man becomes excited, his penis grows stiff. It is at this point that a CONDOM can be put on the penis (see also BIRTH CONTROL and SAFER SEX).

Once it is erect the penis can push into the vagina – it may need a helping hand to direct it. In order for both partners to have an ORGASM, the tips of the clitoris and of the penis have to receive stimulation. For the male, this is achieved as the penis slides up and down inside the vagina. Some girls and women may need to use a hand (their own or their partner's) to stimulate their clitoris – especially if she is lying on her back with him on top in what's known as MISSIONARY POSITION. This is just one of many sexual positions.

Most couples find that if they both move their bodies in rhythm with each other they feel increased sexual pleasure. These thrusting movements usually get faster as the excitement builds up. At the peak of excitement the male will have an ORGASM and SEMEN spurts out of his penis in four or five bursts. Females don't EJACULATE in this way, but when they reach their CLIMAX they also have an orgasm.

After he's COME, the male's penis returns to its normal limp state.

(known as DETUMESCENCE) and it may take an hour or more before he can get another erection. After she's come, she may feel ready and able to have one or more orgasms immediately after (see MULTIPLE ORGASM).

Many couples think that the 'proper' way to enjoy sexual intercourse is for both to reach orgasm together. But this rarely happens. And it's not always so great when it does — when you're in the middle of your own orgasm it isn't easy to help your partner reach theirs. As long as both partners want and enjoy what's happening to them there's no such thing as a wrong or right way to have sex. What's happening biologically is far less important than how you feel about yourself and your partner.

sexually transmitted disease (STD)

Sometimes called a VENEREAL DISEASE (from Venus, the Latin goddess of love), this is any illness that can be passed from one partner to another during ORAL, VAGINAL, or ANAL SEX. The most serious STD, for which there is still no cure is HIV, the virus that can lead to AIDS.

Some STDs such as SYPHILIS and GONORRHOEA can only be transmitted during sex. Others, such as THRUSH and some types of URETHRITIS, can be sexually transmitted but they can also have non-sexual causes. Although there are various different ways of getting a sexually transmitted disease, it's extremely unlikely that anyone has ever caught one from a dirty toilet seat — a well-known myth.

People don't like admitting that they've got an STD. This has a lot to do with feelings of guilt about sex. If you don't think of sex as a perfectly normal part of life (which it is) then you might think of a sexually transmitted disease as some sort of divine punishment for being 'dirty', 'naughty' or 'sinful'. But no illness is ever a punishment. A sexually transmitted disease is not caught by being 'bad', or by having sex with a great number of different people (see PROMISCUOUS). You get it simply by having sex with just one person who happens to be infected with the disease.

The most common STD are AIDS/HIV, CANDIDA ALBICANS (also called thrush, monilias, yeast infection, candidosis or candidiasis), CHANCROID (soft sore or soft chancre), CHLAMYDIA, CYSTITIS (this can also be a symptom of another STD), GARDNERELLA, genital WARTS, gonorrhoea, HEPATITIS B, HERPES, syphilis, TRICHOMONIASIS, urethritis (also called non-specific, non-gonococcal and post-gonococcal urethritis), PUBIC LICE (or CRABS).

You can find out more about each one elsewhere in this book. If you or your partner have, or think you have, any of these infections you should both go immediately to your doctor or, if you want to be more anonymous, to a SPECIAL CLINIC which deals only with STDs. Don't delay – some STDs have only very mild symptoms, others have none at all. But STDs never go away by themselves. Both partners should always go for treatment to prevent a ping-pong effect of passing the infection back and forth to each other.

shag

Since the eighteenth century 'to shag' has meant to have SEXUAL INTERCOURSE with a woman. Around the same time, 'a shag' was slang for a performer of the sexual act – almost always the male. *The Dictionary of the Vulgar Tongue* (vulgar in this sense meaning 'of the common people' rather than rude or coarse – see Glossary) which has been a wonderful source of 'pickpocket eloquence' since it was first published in 1785, translates the sentence, 'he is but bad shag' as 'he is no able woman's man'. Today this would be probably be translated as 'he can't get it up' (see ERECTION).

The slang use of shag probably comes from its Standard English use for 'to shake or toss about' which may explain why it meant 'to MASTURBATE' in 1900. ('To toss off' has been a male slang term for what *The Dictionary of the Vulgar Tongue* defined as 'manual pollution' since the 1780s.) Shag is also used to mean 'tired' – someone who is 'shagged out' may or may not have been up all night having sex.

sheath

The use of the word sheath for a CONDOM makes a connection between sex and violence since the standard definition of a sheath is 'a close-fitting cover, especially for the blade of a weapon or tool'.

shit See FAECES.

short hairs

When someone says that they have a person 'by the short hairs' or 'by the short and curlies' it means they're in a ruling, superior or victorious position over them. PUBIC HAIRS are short and curly. The terms imply that you are holding your enemy so close and in such an intimate place that they can't escape.

shrimping

Some couples give (and receive) sexual pleasure from gently sucking their partner's toes, an activity known as shrimping.

sixty-nine See SOIXANTE-NEUF.

slag

To a metallurgist, slag is a piece of left-over or refuse matter that has been separated from a metal in the process of smelting. The various slang uses of 'slag' have all been influenced by the idea of 'refuse'. In the eighteenth century 'slagger' was a term of contempt for a worthless, cowardly fellow. Two hundred years later it meant a BROTHEL-keeper (see MADAM). 'A slag' has been a rough or brutal person, a contemptible person, a small-time criminal, a female PROSTITUTE, and a PROMISCUOUS girl or woman. By the 1980s slag was probably the commonest insult used by teenagers to refer to a girl's sexual reputation. There isn't a similar word which insults a boy (see DOUBLE STANDARD).

In New Zealand, slag has been part of the vocabulary of racists who use it to mean a white girl who lives with or is friendly with Maori people (see MISCEGENATION).

slash

If you slash someone or something you make slits or cuts with violent, usually random, movements. In British slang a male who is 'taking a slash' is having a pee. 'A slash' also means the VAGINA and is often used to refer to a girl or woman, especially one who's seen by men as a SEX OBJECT. The word probably comes from an Old French word meaning 'to break' and since slash also has the sense of 'to make one's way by cutting down obstacles' the connection with vagina may have something to do with ideas about breaking the HYMEN in a VIRGIN.

It's clearly SEXIST to describe a female purely in terms of her vagina. It's even more offensive when people use words such as slash, slit, gash, etc, which make a strong connection between male aggression and passive female sexuality. Films that make a point of glorifying MACHO sexual violence towards women are known as 'slash and gash' (or 'slice 'n dice') movies.

slattern

Historically, a girl or woman who was untidy and slovenly in person, habits or surrounding was referred to as 'slatternly'. See SLUT.

slim

This is the name given to AIDS in East Africa because those with AIDS often experience severe weight loss.

slit

This has been slang for the VULVA since the seventeenth century. In the 1920s it began to be used as a disreputable term for the CLITORIS, probably because it rhymes with 'clit'. Like SLASH and gash, slit makes a connection between the female PUDENDA and male violence – the standard definition of the verb to slit is 'to cut or tear into long narrow strips' which has its origins in an Old German word meaning 'to tear apart'.

slut

In the Middle Ages, 'sluttish' was a word used to describe both women and men who were so dirty and untidy in their dress and habits that they were disgustingly repulsive. By the mid-fifteenth century 'a slut' was a PROMISCUOUS girl or woman. Towards the end of the sixteenth century 'sluttish' was no longer used of men.

Like the words SCRUBBER and SLATTERN, 'slut' is an insulting name for any female who doesn't look 'ladylike' and who appears to enjoy sex. In the USA, however, 'slutty' means sexually attractive – the female version of 'hunky'.

smear test See CERVICAL SMEAR TEST.

smegma

This is the name given to the cheesy, fatty substance produced by glands under the FORESKIN of the PENIS and around the CLITORIS and inner lips (see LABIA) of the female GENITALS. Boys and men often call it COCK CHEESE because if it's not washed off it begins to smell unpleasantly like old cheese. The medical purpose of male CIRCUM-CISION is to get rid of the glands that produce smegma. However, many doctors now believe that all that needs to be done to prevent smegma from building up is to keep the genital area clean. This was something that the Greeks and Romans presumably realized, since 'smegma' in Latin means 'detergent or soap', and in Greek it means 'to wash off or clean'.

snog

In 1937, men in Britain's Royal Air Force talked of 'going snogging' when they went courting. When an airman went out on a date he presumably put on his best clothes, giving 'snogged up' as RAF slang for being dressed up. By the late 1950s 'snog' had left the RAF and was widely used, especially among jazz and peace-loving beatniks, to mean 'to flirt'. Since then it's mostly been used by British teenagers to mean KISSING, cuddling, and PETTING.

snuff movie

The majority of PORNOGRAPHIC films aim to TITILLATE their mostly male audiences by mixing sex with violence and by portraying women as passive victims of RAPE and torture. This type of film is known as a 'SLASH and gash' or 'slice 'n' dice' movie. The female characters are often murdered. A film in which the female playing the part is actually killed is called a 'snuff movie' – her life is 'snuffed out'. Some people believe such movies have actually been made, but it has never been proved.

sodomy

Sodom is a city mentioned in the Old Testament which God

destroyed because it was so full of corruption. Most people use sodomy to mean ANAL INTERCOURSE but technically it means a variety of sexual practices which are or have been illegal, including intercourse of any kind with animals (see BESTIALITY, ZOOPHILIA), as well as anal intercourse and ORAL SEX between human beings.

soft sore or **soft chancre** (shanker)

These are terms for the ulcer that forms on the GENITALS of someone suffering from the VENEREAL DISEASE called CHANCROID.

soixante-neuf (*swahss*-ant nerf)

When a couple are both giving each other ORAL SEX (see FELLATIO and CUNNILINGUS) at the same time it's known by the French term '*soixante-neuf*' or, in translation, 'sixty-nine'. Put 69 on its side and it becomes clear. Do the same thing to 66 or 99 and you get the explanation for these slang terms for ANAL SEX.

solicit

A PROSTITUTE who publicly accosts a prospective customer with an offer of sex (for money) is said to solicit, or importune, him. It comes from the Latin word meaning 'to disturb'.

spanish fly See APHRODISIAC.

spanking

For many people, bottoms are an EROGENOUS ZONE which give sexual pleasure for some when touched, stroked and spanked. The term 'slap and tickle' for playful lovemaking suggests that a bit of friendly bottom-smacking between two lovers is enjoyed by many couples. Some people, however, can only get sexual excitement and satisfaction if they are spanked very hard or whipped. See also MASOCHISM, SADISM, SADO-MASOCHISM and PERVERSION.

special clinic

If you have, or think you have, a SEXUALLY TRANSMITTED DISEASE, you can go to a special clinic – 'special' in the sense that they specialize in treating STDs. They're also known as VENEREAL DISEASE (VD) clinics, Genito-urinary (GU) clinics, and Sexually Transmitted Disease (STD) clinics and may be listed in the phone book under any of these names. They're widely referred to as POX clinics, but they don't just deal with SYPHILIS or other venereal diseases.

You don't have to be referred to one of these clinics by your own doctor and you don't have to give your name or age if you don't want to (they get a lot of Mr and Mrs Smiths). You can walk into some off the street, while for others you have to make an appointment. They may ask you for the names and addresses of your recent lover(s) which you don't have to reveal, but the only reason they want to know is so that they can contact them to ensure they get cured and don't, perhaps unknowingly, pass on a disease to another partner. This is known as 'contact tracing'.

Most people report that the doctors and nurses in these clinics are not interested in anything other than curing disease – you won't get a moral lecture. You may get some counselling on how to cope with the illness you've got – especially if you have, or think you have, HIV or AIDS. They're very good places to go to if you don't want to tell your own doctor or if you want to have an HIV test and don't want anyone to know.

speculum (*spek*-yu-lum)
When a doctor needs to examine the VAGINA of a girl or woman, she or he uses a special instrument called a speculum, which gets its name from the Latin for 'to look at'. This is inserted into the vagina to hold its walls apart and enables the doctor to see the CERVIX. They come in various sizes and are made of either plastic or metal. The doctor will rub some LUBRICATING jelly on it first to make sure it slips in gently. A really thoughtful doctor will warm it first.

sperm/spermatozoon (spur-mat-toe-*zoe*-on)
Sperm is short for spermatozoon, formed from the Greek words for 'seed' and 'animal'. In the plural you can talk of 'sperm', 'sperms' and 'spermatozoa'. A sperm is the male GAMETE which, when united with

the OVUM (the female gamete), creates a new life. They are about five microns long and two to three microns thick and consist of an oval- or spade-shaped head and a slender whip-like tail. The oval-headed sperm carry a female, or X, sex chromosome. The spade-headed ones carry a male, or Y, sex chromosome.

sperm bank See ARTIFICIAL INSEMINATION BY DONOR (AID).

spermicide (sperm-ee-side)
Any word with '-cide' at the end is going to involve death as it's from the Latin for 'cut down, kill'. A spermicide is a CONTRACEPTIVE that kills sperm. It comes in various forms – creams, jellies, PESSARIES, and aerosol foams. They should never be used without another form of BIRTH CONTROL such as a CONDOM or DIAPHRAGM. Spermicides which contain NONOXYNOL 9 or octoxynol are best because this chemical can also kill HIV, the virus that can lead to AIDS. Unfortunately, many people report that Nonoxynol causes irritation of the vagina or penis. If this happens you'll have to try another type of spermicide. It's also important to make sure your spermicide is water-based since any other sort can make the condom perish.

sponge
Girls and women who don't particularly mind if they get PREGNANT (due to its lower effectiveness rating) can use a CONTRACEPTIVE sponge which is impregnated with a SPERMICIDE. These look like a cross between a mushroom and a large marshmallow and have a loop attached to help pull them out. They have to be quickly placed under the tap first to make the spermicide effective and then pushed into the VAGINA, right up to the CERVIX, before SEXUAL INTERCOURSE. They should be kept in place for about eight hours. Sponges do not necessarily prevent the spread of SEXUALLY TRANSMITTED DISEASE and are not recommended for those practising SAFER SEX.

spunk
In the eighteenth century, this was slang for 'mettle, spirit, pluck' perhaps from the Gaelic *spong* meaning 'something with which you

light a fire'. In the nineteenth century it became slang for SEMEN, presumably because courage and virility were commonly thought to be closely connected.

Towards the end of the nineteenth century the rhyming slang term 'Victoria Monk' was used for spunk. This came from the name of a character in an infamous nineteenth-century PORNOGRAPHIC novel whose name was actually Maria Monk but was confused with the name of a well-known music-hall singer called Victoria Monks, famous for singing 'Won't you come home Bill Bailey?'.

statutory rape

This is the American legal term for the crime committed by a male if he has SEXUAL INTERCOURSE with a girl who is below the AGE OF CONSENT. This age varies from state to state. The punishment for statutory rape ranges from a fine to life imprisonment – although the age of the male is usually taken into consideration and an older man would be given a heavier sentence than a teenager (see LOLITA).

sterile (*ster*-rile)

Sterile, INFERTILE, BARREN, unfruitful and IMPOTENT all mean 'unable to produce a child'. Sterile and infertile imply an inability to PROCREATE because of some deficiency; but 'sterile' also means 'uncreative'. Barren and unfruitful emphasize childlessness in a human, but 'barren' also means 'unrewarding'. Impotence refers particularly to a man's inability to achieve or maintain an ERECTION and also means 'powerlessness'.

Being sterile is different from being impotent which means being unable to COPULATE. For instance, a EUNUCH (a man who has had his testicles removed) is sterile but not necessarily impotent. And some people are impotent for psychological reasons but become fertile if their emotional problems can be overcome.

sterilization

If a woman or a man decides they don't want to have children they can be sterilized. This is an operation involving cutting and tying or blocking the FALLOPIAN TUBES of a woman and cutting and tying or blocking two tiny tubes called the SEMINAL DUCTS in a man's testicles (see VASECTOMY). Sterilization is meant to last for ever and can seldom be reversed so it's mostly performed on someone who already has children or a woman for whom it would be dangerous to get pregnant.

straight

This was originally used by HOMOSEXUALS as a term of contempt for a HETEROSEXUAL. It may have been a form of revenge on hetero-sexuals who referred to GAY women and men as 'bent'. In recent years 'straight' appears to be losing some of this contempt and becoming the opposite of 'gay', which is mostly used very neutrally without any sense of insult.

Other slang terms for a heterosexual include breeder (implying gays don't have children), citizen (gays have never been granted the same citizen rights as straights), VANILLA (a term of contempt – vanilla tastes boring), right-handed (left-handedness is seen to be less 'normal').

sugar daddy/mummy

'Sugar daddy' was originally a Hollywood term for an oldish man who spent a lot of money on a young woman, usually in return for sex. Maybe the 'sugar' was the coating on the bitter sexual pill. Other similar slang terms include JOHN, old man, poppa, santa claus, sugar papa.

In the 1970s, LESBIANS and feminists who refused to accept that only men ever had the money or the desire to support a woman, invented the term 'sugar mummy'. The inequality of incomes be-tween the sexes (on average women earn only two-thirds of what men earn) may explain why there are very few, if any, sugar mummies around.

syphilis

This is a serious VENEREAL DISEASE which is sexually transmitted. It was first noted during the French-Neopolitan war of 1495 when it was known as the 'French sickness' by the Italians and the 'Neopolitan sickness' by the French. It was understood that the disease was spread by SEXUAL INTERCOURSE but the cause was thought to be the conjunction of Saturn (an unlucky planet) and Jupiter in the sign of the Scorpio and the house of Mars (another unlucky planet) in 1484.

Spanish doctors noted that the POX epidemic which swept through Europe in the late 1490s coincided with the return of Christopher Columbus from his voyage to the Americas in 1494 and blamed the women of the island of Hispaniola in the Indies who gave it to the Spanish sailors. In 1530 an Italian doctor named Girolamo Fracastero wrote a poem in Latin about a shepherd named Syphilis who offended the Sun God. His punishment was the venereal disease which the local peasants named 'syphilis' in memory of the first person to suffer from it. But until the eighteenth century most people used the word 'pox'.

Syphilis is mostly spread by sexual intercourse (anal or vaginal). The first symptom appears nine to ninety days after the infection has entered the body. During the first very infectious stage a painless sore which isn't always noticeable appears on or near the vagina or penis and sometimes near the anus or mouth. This sore disappears after about a month but the bacteria remains in the body. The next stage develops from a week to six months later. Symptoms may include a copper-coloured rash which sometimes covers the entire body, a mild fever, swollen joints, and a sore throat, often mistaken for influenza. There are no outward signs during the final stage but if left untreated syphilis will result in paralysis, blindness, madness and eventually death.

Doctors at a SPECIAL CLINIC, which deals with SEXUALLY TRANSMITTED DISEASES, can cure syphilis with penicillin or another antibiotic for those allergic to penicillin. The treatment usually involves at least two follow-up blood tests to make sure it has been cured, during which time there should be no sex. But prevention is better than cure: a CONDOM is the best means of preventing syphilis as well as all other sexually transmitted diseases.

T

taboo

This is a social custom of avoiding certain words, subjects, or actions because they are considered embarrassing, offensive or OBSCENE. It comes from a Polynesian word literally meaning 'marked off' where it had a religious significance. Sigmund Freud, the founder of psychoanalysis, defined taboo like this:

'On the one hand it means to us sacred, consecrated; but on the other hand it means uncanny, dangerous, forbidden, and unclean.'

A taboo act in one society may be socially acceptable in another. It is taboo, for example among Orthodox Jews, for a man to have SEXUAL INTERCOURSE with a woman while she is having her PERIOD. For the Yucatec and Mayan Indians, having sex out of doors is taboo. In Western society, adultery, ANAL SEX, BESTIALITY, and the use of certain gestures and so-called FOUR-LETTER WORDS are often considered taboo. This doesn't stop people from breaking these taboos. (See also Glossary.)

tail

In the fourteenth century 'tail' became a slang term for a PENIS. 'Tail' also used to refer to the female sex organs but this came from the Old French word *taille* meaning 'a notch, cut, nick' (see SLASH, SLIT). In the eighteenth century it had the sense of HARLOT. 'A bit of tail' became slang for SEXUAL INTERCOURSE and since the nineteenth century for a woman seen as a sex object.

tampon

These finger-like wads of cotton-wool which are inserted into the VAGINA are a convenient way of absorbing the MENSTRUAL flow during a PERIOD. Inside the vagina they expand and fit snugly so that nothing shows and, as long as they're changed fairly regularly, nothing leaks. They have a string hanging from one end to make them easy to pull out and come in different sizes with the mini or regular ones for light days and large or super ones for when the flow is heavy. Those who like tampons say that they're less bulky and a lot easier than SANITARY TOWELS, because they can be flushed away.

If the HYMEN has not been broken it may be difficult at first to push a tampon in, but it usually slips in more easily if you smear some LUBRICATING jelly on it. Tampons can't get out of the vagina except via the way they entered. Some girls feel a bit squeamish about touching themselves and panic if they can't find the string to pull them out. And it's easy to forget that you've got one in – you forget about the first and then push in another. If this happens, don't panic. But don't leave it in either. If you're really stuck, you can always ask your doctor to pull it out – they're quite used to doing this.

Tampons may be implicated in a rare but serious disease called TOXIC SHOCK SYNDROME.

tart

In the middle of the nineteenth century this was a term of affection used by a man for his girlfriend. It may have been rhyming slang or a shortening of 'sweetheart'. Like honey-bun, sweetie-pie, cupcake and other similar words the idea behind calling a female lover a tart seems to have been the romantic belief that girls are, like the nursery rhyme says, 'sugar and spice and all things nice'.

By the beginning of the twentieth century a tart was not so nice; the word degenerated (see Glossary) firstly to mean a fast, LOOSE or sexually PROMISCUOUS female and later a PROSTITUTE. By the 1930s a woman who was 'tarted up' was over-dressed in showy, flashy clothes. During the Second World War (1939–1945) 'tart' became slang for a CATAMITE, or a male prostitute. Today, 'a tart' is a woman who is considered cheap and loose.

test-tube baby See FERTILIZATION.

testicle/testis

Also called 'testes' (the singular is testis), the testicles are the two SPERM-producing glands inside the SCROTUM. The word is from the Latin for 'little witness' perhaps because these male sex organs (also known as GONADS) are evidence, or witness, of manliness (see VIRILITY). In ancient times men used to swear an oath by putting their hands on their testicles; EUNUCHS couldn't give evidence in law because they had no testicles (see CASTRATION).

Every boy should get to know how his testicles feel so that if any unusual lump appears he can go immediately to his doctor; CANCER of the testicles is increasing but can be cured if treated at an early stage. The best place to examine them is in the bath or shower when he's feeling warm and relaxed. On top of each testicle gland is a mass of soft tissue called the EPIDIDYMIS. This can be gently separated from the testicle. A lump (which may only be a harmless cyst) feels much harder.

Slang terms include bollocks, BALLS, *cojones* (from the Spanish), diamonds, family jewels (see SCHMUCK), jingle-berries, goolies, nuts, rocks.

testosterone See HORMONE.

thrush

Thrush is a vaginal infection caused by the fungus called candida albicans. This fungus normally lives in the mouth and intestines of most people but occasionally sets up an infection which forms itchy white patches in the mouth or VAGINA which may look like cottage cheese and smell like baking bread. With a bit of imagination these white patches could be thought to look like the white speckles on the throat of a thrush. The word '*candida*' comes from the Latin for 'white, a glistening' ('candidates' in ancient Roman elections always wore white robes). The infection is also known as yeast infection because the candida fungus is related to the yeast fungus.

Candida is normally kept under control by the body's natural bacteria. But if these are destroyed by, for instance, antibiotics taken for some other illness, the fungus can start to increase and will need antibiotic treatment itself. This infection can spread between sexual partners (see SEXUALLY TRANSMITTED DISEASE). Symptoms can include itchiness, a thickish white discharge and is sometimes accompanied by CYSTITIS. If one partner has it, the chances are that the other one will also get it although not everyone has any symptoms. Both should go to a doctor or SPECIAL CLINIC, and should use a CONDOM until it has cleared up. Some women find that a daily DOUCHE of natural yoghurt helps to relieve the symptoms.

tit

Since the seventeenth century 'tits' or 'titties' have been slang for the female BREASTS. It may be a misspelling of 'teat' meaning 'nipple'. In Shakespeare's time 'a tit' was a vulgar term for a young woman and by the nineteenth century it meant a HARLOT. In this sense it may have come from the fourteenth-century sense of 'small horse', in much the same way that a sexually attractive young woman is sometimes called a filly. (See RIDE for other horse terms.) Over the years tit has also been used for the female PUDENDUM, a PENIS, and an idiot. An extremely annoying person is said to 'get on my tits'.

titillate

This word comes from the Latin for 'to tickle' or 'to arouse SENSUALLY'. A thing or person that titillates someone gives mild sexual pleasure or arousal.

tomboy

When 'tomboy' entered English in the mid-fifteenth century it meant a rude, boisterous boy. Within a hundred years it was a pejorative term for a 'sexually wild or PROMISCUOUS young woman. The Swiss Protestant leader John Calvin (1509–1564) used the term in this sense:

'Sainte Paule meaneth that women must not be impudent, they must not be tomboyes, to be shorte, they must not bee unchast.'

In *Cymbeline* Shakespeare used the word to mean a WHORE. A slang dictionary published in 1700 defined 'tomboy' as 'a Ramp or Tom rig'. 'Rig' meant a WANTON young woman and 'ramp' was a bold, vulgar ill-behaved female.

In the nineteenth century, perhaps influenced by enlightened feminist attitudes towards education, 'tomboyism' was defined as a tendency in girls who showed a wholesome delight in rushing around at full speed, playing at active games, climbing trees, rowing boats, making dirt-pies, and the like.

It's clearly a lot better for a girl to be a tomboy today than it was a few hundred years ago. But the term reveals a DOUBLE STANDARD at work. It's acceptable for a girl to behave 'like a boy' but if a boy acts like a girl he gets condemned as a 'sissy' (shortened from 'sister'). See also FEMININITY and MASCULINITY.

tool

This may originate in an Old English word for 'to prepare land for sewing' (see SEED). Around the time Queen Elizabeth I came to the throne in the mid-sixteenth century, tool was beginning to be used as a slang term for a PENIS. This is probably connected to the formal sense of tool as 'a hand-held instrument to help do a particular kind of job'.

toxic shock syndrome (TSS)

This rare but serious disease, from which a number of women have died, mainly affects MENSTRUATING women under 30 who are using TAMPONS. CONTRACEPTIVE devices that go into the VAGINA (such as the SPONGE or DIAPHRAGM) may also be connected with TSS. It's probably caused by bacteria which infects some part of the body, often the vagina, and produces poisons (toxins) that go into the bloodstream. The syndrome, or group of symptoms, include a high temperature, vomiting, diarrhoea, a sudden drop in blood pressure which may lead to shock, and a rash like a sunburn which appears on the trunk of the body, the palms of the hands and the soles of the feet, and which eventually peels.

Any girl or woman who gets any of these symptoms during her PERIOD should remove her tampon and go to her doctor or the casualty department of the nearest hospital immediately. It's also important to drink lots of water. TSS can be cured by antibiotics.

toy boy

This is roughly the male equivalent of the term 'doll', which suggests a sexually attractive young woman who exists only for a man to play with. Any male or young man who has an older woman for a lover – not something that is easily accepted in our society – may find himself negatively referred to as a 'toy boy'. Toy boys may be pretty, but the term suggests that they aren't very bright. (See also BIMBO.)

transsexual

Some people grow up feeling they're not the right sex; a girl may feel that she's really a boy and a boy feels like he's really a girl. These feelings may be the result of HORMONE imbalances which result in what are known as 'gender-identity disorders' or it may be connected to the way in which they were brought up. If these feelings get to be almost unbearably strong, some people seek help from psychiatrists and surgeons to change their sex. With hormone treatment a male is able to develop breasts and a surgeon can help create something similar to a VAGINA. Females who want to be men (this is more rare) can be helped by having their breasts removed and something a bit like a penis can be created for them from their LABIA.

Although the medical profession can help them live the sort of life they want, in most countries the law is unhelpful. In many countries, for instance, transsexuals are not allowed to change the GENDER identity on their birth certificate, nor can they officially marry someone of what for them has become the 'opposite' sex.

transvestite

This is the name given to someone who feels compelled to wear the clothes of the opposite GENDER, informally called CROSS-DRESSING and wearing drag. For women today it's no problem. But a man who wants to wear high-heeled shoes, tights, dresses and make-up often finds himself in trouble with people who can't bear anyone to blur the boundaries between what's generally thought to be FEMININE and MASCULINE. A transvestite differs from a TRANSSEXUAL in that she or he only wants the clothes of the opposite sex, they don't necessarily want to change sex. It's widely, but incorrectly, assumed that most transvestites are HOMOSEXUAL – some are, some aren't. It's difficult to see what possible harm transvestites can cause but police frequently harass them and arrest them for insulting behaviour.

tribade (try-bad) See LESBIAN, RUB.

Trichomoniasis (tryk-o-mon-*eye*-as-siss)
This is the disease caused by infection with *Trichomonas*, which is a one-cell parasite found in both females and males. Symptoms in females include a greenish or grey foamy discharge from the VAGINA, swelling of the whole vaginal area, and pain when making love (see DYSPAREUNIA). Males usually have no symptoms or they may get an infection known as URETHRITIS, a white discharge from their PENIS and pain when they urinate. Whether or not there are any symptoms, 'trich' is usually a SEXUALLY TRANSMITTED DISEASE meaning that it's spread by SEXUAL INTERCOURSE. Emotional stress can cause symptoms to flare up or recur. If either partner thinks they may have trich both should go to their doctor or a SPECIAL CLINIC for treatment – usually a strong antibiotic. Use a CONDOM when having sex until it's been cured.

trick
Around the time of the First World War (1914–1918) this became American slang among PROSTITUTES for a male customer – perhaps because they often had to FAKE an ORGASM.

troilism (*troy*-lism)
From the Latin word for three, sometimes called triolism, this is a triangular sexual activity in which all three people make love to each other at the same time. It usually means that two of the

partners are having ORAL SEX while one of them is also having GENITAL sex with the third.

Trojan

This is the American trade-name for a popular brand of CONDOM. Like DUREX in the UK, it's widely used as a synonym (see Glossary) for 'condom'. The imagery of the word 'trojan' is baffling: the Trojans were warriors from the ancient city of Troy who for years bravely resisted the invading Greek army until they were finally tricked by a huge wooden horse containing enemy soldiers.

tumescence (tyoo-*mess*-ence)

From the Latin for 'swollen', this is the formal term for an ERECTION. The opposite is DETUMESCENCE.

twat (twat or twot)

Since the middle of the seventeenth century this has been a vulgar term for the VULVA. It may come from a fifteenth-century word, *twachelle* meaning 'a passage or path between hedges' – presumably from the image of the VAGINA surrounded by PUBIC HAIR. In the eighteenth century 'twat-scourer' was slang for a gynaecologist.

The UK poet Robert Browning (1812–1889) made an embarrassing mistake about the meaning of twat. Having read a BAWDY seventeenth-century poem called *Vanity of Vanities* which has the line, 'They talk'd of his having a Cardinall's Hat, They'd send him an old Nun's Twat', Browning assumed 'twat' was a nun's head-dress.

In the twentieth century twat became mild male slang for the VAGINA, similar to the word PRAT. Twat can also mean the buttocks of either sex (see FANNY).

U

uranism

This is an obsolete (see Glossary) term for HOMOSEXUALITY. It was coined by the German sexologist Karl Heinrich Ulrichs in 1862 from the word Urania, meaning Celestial One, a title given to Aphrodite, the Greek goddess of heavenly love.

urethra

This is the tube through which URINE passes as it leaves the bladder. In the female it's fairly short and ends in the urethral opening, sometimes called 'pee hole', which is between the CLITORIS and the opening to the VAGINA. The urethra in males is longer, as it runs through the middle of the penis ending at the tip of the GLANS. It carries SEMEN as well as urine.

urethritis

This is an inflammation of the URETHRA. Symptoms include extreme pain when peeing, sometimes a pus-like discharge, and slight fever.

Urethritis is most often spread by SEXUAL INTERCOURSE (see SEXUALLY TRANSMITTED DISEASE) and may indicate GONORRHOEA. Depending on whether the patient has gonorrhoea or not, this infection is called Non-Specific Urethritis (NSU), Non-Gonococcal Urethritis (NGU) or Post-Gonococcal Urethritis (PGU). Anyone with the above symptoms should go to their doctor or SPECIAL CLINIC. Once it has been accurately diagnosed doctors can cure it with the appropriate antibiotic. Sexual partners should use a CONDOM until completely cured.

urine (*yoor*-in)

From the Greek, this is the waste fluid from the body, informally called wee, pee or piss. It collects in the bladder and then passes down through the URETHRA and out through the urethral opening. In medieval English urine was called *waeter* from which we get the term 'passing water' or urinating.

Some people find urine a sexual turn on and enjoy what are known as 'water sports' or 'golden showers'. This may involve peeing on or being peed on as a part of FOREPLAY. The technical term for this is urinism. If someone can only get sexually excited by urine it's considered to be a psychosexual disorder called urolagnia or urophilia.

Urine is one of the body fluids which may contain HIV, the virus that can lead to AIDS. If there is any likelihood of urine coming into contact with the VAGINA or a cut or open sore somewhere on the body of a partner, sex games involving urine shouldn't be played (see SAFER SEX).

uterus See WOMB.

V

vagina (vaj-*jie*-nah)

In Latin *vagina* means sheath or scabbard. In his play *Pseudolus*, Plautus (250–184 BC) made a punning reference to the vagina: 'Did the soldier's sword fit your sheath?'. When translated into English in the seventeenth century it was thought this was the actual Latin word for this female sex organ and has been used as the anatomical term ever since.

The vagina forms a passageway between the CERVIX and the vaginal opening which is placed between the ANUS and the pee-hole in the VULVA on the outside. The vaginal opening may be covered by a thin layer of skin called the HYMEN. Its inner walls are made of soft crinkled muscular membrane that normally touch each other but can stretch to accept a TAMPON during a PERIOD or, during SEXUAL INTERCOURSE to take the full length of an erect PENIS. During childbirth the vagina widens to allow the baby to be born through it which is why it's sometimes also called the 'birth passage'. The walls expand and contract as the waves of pleasure rush through a woman's body when she has an ORGASM.

Although the word vagina technically refers to this internal passage, it's often used to refer to the area of the external female sex organs, which are more correctly called the VULVA.

Slang terms include boat, box, canyon, central cut, chasm, chopped liver, crack, cranny, crevice, ditch, drain, finger pie, front door, gap, gash, glory-hole, golden doughnut, gulf, gully (hole), gutter, hole, honeypot, jellybox, lunch-box, nest, passion pit, pole hole, RAG box (this presumably refers to a sanitary towel), SLASH, SLIT, slot, trench, and stinkpot (not a word likely to make a woman feel good about her own natural smells – see PHEROMONE).

vaginismus (vaj-in-*iz*-mus)

A rare condition that some girls and women suffer from involving a painful spasm of the VAGINA, making SEXUAL INTERCOURSE very unpleasurable and PENETRATION almost impossible. It may be the result of a fear of sex, or because her partner is being too rough or hasn't spent enough time on FOREPLAY.

Jokes or rumours which claim the vagina can clamp tight around the PENIS during sexual intercourse and never let go are not true. Psychiatrists think these stories reflect male anxiety about losing their penis, called CASTRATION complex. The term 'vagina dentata' (literally 'vagina with teeth') is used when talking about this unconscious male fear or FANTASY.

vaginitis (vaj-in-*eye*-tis)

Inflammation of the VAGINA that may be caused by an infection or by physical injury. The vagina can also get sore and inflamed if there isn't enough LUBRICATION during SEXUAL INTERCOURSE. This may depend on the time of the month – some vaginas are naturally a bit drier when a girl or woman has her PERIOD. Lubricating jelly, which can be bought from the chemist, or a lubricated CONDOM prevent the vagina from getting sore and inflamed. Saliva works well also.

vanilla

The *vanilla planifolia* is a species of climbing orchid, the pods of which are used to make an extract to flavour ice-cream, chocolate and various puddings. In the eighteenth century Madame Pompadour, the MISTRESS of Louis XV, swore by vanilla as an APHRODISIAC. In the twentieth century, because of its association with white ice-cream and its bland flavour, it became slang for a white person, especially a white woman, a sexually unimaginative HETEROSEXUAL, and an adjective for conventional, STRAIGHT sex.

There's no connection between these meanings and the origins of this word, but 'vanilla' comes from the Latin word meaning 'sheath' that gave the English language its word for the female sex organ, VAGINA.

vas deferens See SEMINAL DUCTS.

vasectomy

This is an operation to STERILIZE a man by cutting his SEMINAL DUCTS (formally called the vas deferens). This prevents the SPERM from ever leaving the TESTICLES, where they are produced. A man who has had a vasectomy continues to EJACULATE normally but his SEMEN does not contain any sperm. The operation is usually irreversible, so it is only performed on men who are certain they will not want children in the future.

venereal disease (ven-*ear*-ee-al) See SEXUALLY TRANSMITTED DISEASE.

vibrator See DILDO.

virgin (ver-jin)

A female or a male who has never had SEXUAL INTERCOURSE is called a virgin. So is Mary, the mother of Jesus, who is supposed to have become pregnant in a strictly non-sexual way via the Holy Spirit. But in ancient mythology 'Virgin' was a title given to various goddesses many of whom had several lovers and children to prove it. The title indicated an independent woman who had the right to have lovers, or not, as she chose. In ancient Greece even a PROSTITUTE could be called virgin. They were clearly not 'virgins' in the present sense. It seems that virgin comes from the Greek term *virgo intacta* which actually meant 'unmarried woman' but was misunderstood by medieval English translators. See also CHERRY, HYMEN, MAIDENHEAD.

virgin birth

This stems from Christian belief that Mary, the mother of Jesus, never had SEXUAL INTERCOURSE. See also ARTIFICIAL INSEMINATION BY DONOR (AID).

voyeur

This is French for 'one who looks'. When someone, usually a man, gets sexually AROUSED by watching girls and women when they're naked or undressing and couples making love he is called a voyeur or, informally, a PEEPING TOM. It's a form of sexual HARASSMENT and it is a crime. A little curiosity is natural, but if someone can only get sexual gratification in this way it's treated as a pyschosexual disorder.

vulva

The vulva is a formal term for the external female sex organs which include the MONS VENERIS, the CLITORIS, the inner and outer lips, or LABIA, and the opening to the VAGINA. The Anglo-Saxon word for the vulva was CUNT, but once this became a TABOO word, it became the vulva, cunnus or PUDENDUM – perhaps because anatomical Latin terms sounded more 'proper'. In its original Latin, vulva actually meant WOMB.

W

wally (*woll*-ee)

Slang for a stupid or incompetent person. In nineteenth-century London, 'wally' was cockney slang for a cucumber pickled in salty water; calling someone a wally is the same as saying they're a silly PRICK. In the USA, a silly person is sometimes called a 'dill', which may be short for DILDO or may be a reference to a dill pickle, which is a small cucumber pickled in vinegar and the dill herb.

wank

This is the most popular UK term for MASTURBATION. No one knows where the word comes from but since it was spelled 'whank' in the nineteenth century it may have some connection with the slang word 'whang', which was later spelled 'wang', meaning PENIS. It may also be associated with 'whack' and 'bonk' which both have connections with hitting. In the 1920s British air-force men called a bed by the stomach-churning name of 'wank-pit'. 'Wanker' became widely used as a term of abuse for anyone who is fairly stupid and wastes a lot of time – this presumably reflects the false view that masturbating either makes you silly or that it isn't as good as having SEXUAL INTERCOURSE.

The idea of hitting something hard exists in other slang terms for masturbation such as bang the bishop, beat one's meat, beat one's dummy, beat one's log, beat the hog, beat off, cuff or flog one's meat, pound one's meat.

wanton

In the thirteenth century this meant undisciplined, from the Old English prefix (see Glossary) *wan*- meaning 'un-' and *togen* meaning 'brought up'. A hundred years later it had a number of different senses ranging from LASCIVIOUS and LEWD to unrestrained, playful and unruly. By the sixteenth century 'a wanton' was a sexually uncontrolled, devil-inspired woman, or witch. (Witches were well-known to have sex with the devil.) Signs of wantonness included a weakness for fashionable clothes and cosmetics (see JEZEBEL), a taste for dainty food, and a love of luxury and LECHERY. Today, in a sexual sense, wanton means promiscuous.

wart

GENITAL warts are caused by a virus infection. In females they usually appear on the vaginal lips, on the walls of the VAGINA, or on the CERVIX. In males they can appear anywhere on the PENIS or SCROTUM. Both sexes can also get them around the ANUS. They start off as small, painless hard spots which, if left to grow, often develop a cauli-flower-like surface. They tend to increase in number in warm, moist conditions. Because they can be transmitted sexually they are some-times known as venereal warts (see SEXUALLY TRANSMITTED DISEASE), but they can also be transmitted from warts that grow on the hands.

Doctors believe that if warts appear on the cervix there is an increased chance of cervical CANCER. It's important, therefore, that anyone who has, or thinks they have, genital warts should go to their doctor or SPECIAL CLINIC. Both partners should be treated and in the meantime the man should use a CONDOM during lovemaking.

wet dream

A sign of PUBERTY for many boys is their first wet dream, more formally called 'nocturnal emission', which means 'release at night'. This usually comes as a bit of a surprise and lots of boys feel very embarrassed because of the SEMEN that's left on their pyjamas and sheets (it's only a couple of small spoonfuls, but it seems more). Semen doesn't stain if it's washed off within a day or two. It happens to almost every boy and man, especially those who don't have EJACULATIONS by MASTURBATING or having SEXUAL INTERCOURSE.

white slave-trade

This term comes from a popular nineteenth-century play entitled

White Slave, about a girl who was kidnapped by PIMPS and sent abroad to become a PROSTITUTE. The story was set in the 1850s when black slavery was still legal in many parts of the world, including the USA. The white slave-trade was something that much alarmed Victorian society and many of the early feminists and suffragettes campaigned to expose the white slave-traders.

whore (hor)

Meaning PROSTITUTE or HARLOT, this is a very old word in the English language – it first appeared just thirty-four years after William the Conqueror invaded Britain in 1066. It may have come via a Germanic word for someone who commits ADULTERY, and it has connections with a root word meaning 'desire' in ancient Indo-European (see Glossary) from which the Latin *carus* meaning 'dear, beloved' developed. Modern Italian for prostitute is *carogna*, which comes from the same source.

A whore is a woman who sells sex to a man, but it's a very loaded word. You can call someone a prostitute and you may just be describing, very neutrally, the job they do – prostitutes are often referred to as 'working girls'. If a woman is called a whore it carries with it the sense that she is morally despised.

wimp

In the 1920s, male Oxford University students used the phrase 'to go wimping' as slang for 'to be on the look out for females for purposes of sexual gratification'. Today, wimp is widely used as a term of contempt for an ineffectual, soft, silly, weak person. Perhaps because women are expected to be all of these things it's a term mostly reserved for men who, of course, are expected to be effective, hard, determined and strong. However, this 'gender stereotyping' just perpetuates traditional and out-dated barriers between the sexes.

withdrawal See COITUS INTERRUPTUS.

wolf-whistle

This term may originate from a musical term. An ugly-sounding, jarring note made by a keyboard or string instrument is called a wolf, because if a harp did this in medieval times it was due to strings made of wolf gut.

In the nineteenth century the expression 'to see a wolf' meant a SEDUCED or 'fallen' woman, and a wolf was a male seducer (as Little Red Riding Hood discovered in the famous fairy tale). By the 1930s a wolf was a sexually aggressive male, often one who made a habit of seducing the girlfriends and wives of other men.

Some girls and women like a stranger to wolf-whistle while others feel angry or upset because they hate being made to feel as if they are nothing more than a SEX OBJECT. Like all forms of sexual HARASSMENT, you're not consulted about whether you want the attention being paid to you. You'll notice that boys and men mostly do this when they're in a group; they're not interested in the girl or woman they're whistling at or making comments about but are simply showing off to each other. There's little you can do other than ignore it – being ignored is particularly painful to the male ego.

womb (woom)
This is the non-technical word for uterus, the female organ in which a baby develops during PREGNANCY. Womb has had a variety of different meanings over the years. In medieval times it was used for a woman's abdomen, her bowels, and the belly-piece of an animal skin. In early translations of the Bible, the Latin word for 'heart, soul' was translated as 'womb' and an early medical text used this word for one of the cavities of the heart. By the sixteenth century, womb had settled down as the organ that we now know it as, which, as well as being called a uterus (from the Latin), was also called the mother or matrix (from the Latin meaning 'mother'). It has been suggested that 'woman' comes from a combination of womb and man. This presumably reflected the belief that the womb is the essential part of every woman – an unacceptable theory to those who choose not to have children. ('Woman' comes from the Old English word *wifman*, from *wif* meaning 'woman', and *man* meaning 'human'.)

Y

yeast infection See THRUSH.

yellow body See CORPUS LUTEUM.

yoni

In Sanskrit (see Glossary) yoni means both the VULVA and a sacred representation of the vulva. These representations take the form of sculptures in Hindu shrines where it is worshipped, and charms or amulets worn by worshippers. The male equivalent is LINGAM.

z

zoophilia (zoh-o-*fill*-ee-ah) See BESTIALITY.

zygote (*zy*-goat)
This is the OVUM which has been FERTILIZED by a SPERM containing both female and male CHROMOSOMES before it begins to divide. It is the very first stage in the development of a baby.

Glossary

Words in SMALL CAPITALS indicate an entry elsewhere in this list.

acronym A word made up of the initial letters of a phrase, such as AIDS which stands for Acquired Immune Deficiency Syndrome, and is pronounced as a single word, is an acronym. Words such as IUD (pronounced eye-you-dee), which stands for Intrauterine Device (a contraceptive method) are not acronyms because they cannot be pronounced as a single word.

amelioration The process in which the meaning of a word gets better. On the whole, most words do the opposite – they get worse (see DEROGATION). But there are some words which show signs of having ameliorated. 'Bat', for instance, from the seventeenth to the early nineteenth century meant 'prostitute' because, like these small, furry mammals, they come out at dusk. Today it's an uncomplimentary term that is usually applied to a sexually unattractive older woman.

Anglo-Saxon The history of the English language is divided into three periods of which Anglo-Saxon, sometimes called Old English is the earliest. It starts in the fifth century AD (although there aren't any surviving records until the seventh century) and continues up to about the end of the eleventh century after the Norman Conquest in 1066. When someone talks of a 'good old Anglo-Saxon term' they're usually referring to 'cunt', 'prick' or 'fuck' although, of these, only 'prick' dates back to this period.

antonym A word meaning the opposite of another word. 'Good' is the antonym of 'bad' (although not always – see the entry for bad in the main part of this book). This word comes from *anti* meaning 'opposite' and the Greek for 'name'. The antonym of 'antonym' is SYNONYM.

argot French for 'slang'. In English it means a more-or-less secret vocabulary which can be conversational (CANT) or formal (JARGON) used by professional criminals. Their words may get adopted by non-criminals: 'nonce' started off as British prison slang for a male child molester and is now more widely used to mean a pervert or a strongly-disliked person.

cant Conversational, or COLLOQUIAL, vocabulary used and generally understood only by members of a specific occupation, trade, profession, sect, class, age group, interest group, or other sub-group of a culture. It tends to mean the words of those groups of people, like criminals, who are more likely to speak than write. 'Cant' comes from the Latin *cantare* meaning 'to sing'. When it first appeared in the English language in the sixteenth century, it was a verb meaning 'to speak whiningly like a beggar' – presumably because when beggars ask for money they use a sing-song sort of wheedling voice.

coin When a new word is created or invented it is said to be 'coined' from the sense of making or minting a new coin (see NEOLOGISM). Words and phrases can be coined in a number of ways. 'Homosexual' was created in the nineteenth century by adding two words together – 'homos' meaning 'same' and 'sexual' the adjective based on the word 'sex'. Sometimes a word is 'borrowed' rather than 'invented'. For example, 'debauch' was borrowed directly from the French language.

colloquialism Literally, 'conversational'. It's a word not used in formal speech but widely used and completely acceptable in informal circumstances. It can also be a local or regional dialect expression which tends to get passed from mouth to mouth rather than written down. Words sometimes start as a colloquialism and then become part of formal, or STANDARD ENGLISH, or they can travel the other way – 'cock' meaning 'penis' used to be Standard English until the 1940s, when it became a colloquialism.

connotation Words that have one or more meanings (see DENOTE). They can also have implied or suggested meanings which are known as 'connotations'. The literal meaning of 'whore' is a woman who sells sex to male clients, but if a person chooses to use 'whore' instead of 'prostitute' they are usually connoting a sense of moral disapproval about a female who may not, in fact, be a prostitute but has the reputation for being sexually promiscuous.

creole A descendant of European settlers in the West Indies or Central or South America, the white descendants of French settlers in the southern states of the USA, or someone of mixed Afro-American and European descent. It's also the name for any language based on two or more languages, that serves as the native language of its speakers. Many blacks in southern Louisiana in the USA speak a creole which is based on a French dialect. A creole word in the English language is 'poontang' from the French *putain* meaning 'prostitute', which has several (racist) meanings including 'the vagina of a Black or mulatto woman'. Creole probably comes from a Portuguese word meaning 'home-born slave'.

denote A word 'denotes' what it stands for or represents. 'To denote' is another word for 'to mean', from the Latin for 'to mark'.

derogation A derogatory remark expresses a low opinion of someone or something. A word which undergoes derogation loses its original sense of position and status or, in other words, gets worse. The word 'hussy' is a good example. If someone calls a girl or woman a hussy they're almost certainly making a derogatory remark because, not only are they saying she's sexually promiscuous, but they're also saying they disapprove of her behaviour. The word itself has undergone derogation because it was originally an affectionate short form of 'huswif', which originally meant 'female head of a household' in the days when a household was an important economic unit. The opposite (or ANTONYM) of derogation is AMELIORATION.

dictionary A book that explains in alphabetical order the words of a language or words and topics of some special subject or author, from the Latin word meaning 'say'. A lexicon, from the Latin for 'word', is a SYNONYM. Many people think (or are encouraged to think) that dictionaries are totally unbiased. But dictionaries are written by people and anything that a person writes reflects their own views. One dictionary might define a 'dyke' as 'A lesbian, especially a large, mannish, aggressive one, also called a bulldyke or diesel dyke', while another might say, 'Often used to denote that stereotypical mannish lesbian, originally an early twentieth century American slang term of abuse either for any lesbian or for any woman who rejected male advances.' There is a difference.

diminutive This indicates smallness and sometimes lovableness and/or triviality. The '-ette' SUFFIX is often used as a feminine diminutive. In Latin, 'testicle' is the diminutive of 'testis'.

double entendre French for 'double meaning', a word or phrase that has two meanings, one of which is impolite or sexual. Shakespeare was a master of the *double entendre*; in Act 2, Scene iv, lines 93–115 of *Romeo and Juliet* there are at least twelve terms which have a polite sense and are also slang terms for the female and male sex organs or sexual intercourse. See also PUN.

dysphemism A term of speech for an unpleasant or DEROGATORY word or expression which replaces a pleasant or inoffensive one. Someone who does not know who their parents are can be politely described as 'illegitimate' or, dysphemistically, a 'bastard'. The ANTONYM of dysphemism is EUPHEMISM.

etymology The study of the history of words from their earliest recorded appearance (today this might be on television, radio or cinema) tracing their development and changing meanings up to when they become OBSOLETE or to current use.

euphemism A word or expression which is used because it is more mild, vague, or indirect than another that may offend or suggest something unpleasant. It comes from the Greek word meaning 'sounding good'. In Victorian times the word 'breast' was thought to be so offensive that the breast of a chicken was referred to euphemistically as 'white meat'. People who use euphemisms are often criticized, but calling 'a spade a spade' isn't necessarily better than using another term that enriches the language by providing a new and original word or expression.

figurative From the Latin for 'shape', if you use a word or expression in a figurative sense, you use it with a more abstract or imaginative meaning than its ordinary one.

gender In some languages – French, Italian and Spanish, for example – words are divided into feminine and masculine genders. German has three – feminine, masculine and neuter. This doesn't have anything to do with the sex of the object but with how they're spelled. So a word with what language experts call a strong or hard ending like *le vagin* (French for vagina) is said to be masculine while the Spanish word *la barba* meaning beard, is feminine because of its weak or soft ending. In German *das Madchen* meaning 'girl' is neuter. The Italian *il clitoride* meaning 'clitoris' was originally masculine, but in the 1970s, presumably as a result of the Women's Movement, it became *la clitoride* (feminine). The Anglo-Saxon language had three genders but modern English has what's called 'natural gender' which means that objects are labelled according to their sex rather than how they're spelled. Gender comes from the Latin for 'class, kind or species'.

glossary From an Old French word for 'explain', this is a list of explanations of specialist words, usually found at the back of a book – like this one is.

Indo-European English is a fairly recent member of a family of ancient languages known as Indo-European which were spoken in northern Europe, around the Mediterranean, to Ireland in the west and India in the east. Germanic, Greek, Latin and SANSKRIT were all dialects of Indo-European. There is no written evidence of Indo-European but etymologists (see ETYMOLOGY) have been able to identify many of the words of these ancient languages which they believe date back to the third century BC. 'Whore' can be traced back to an Indo-European root word.

jargon The technical or even secret vocabulary of a group of people who all belong to a particular occupation, trade or profession. Also called 'shop talk'. The same word may mean one thing to a group of professionals and something different to those outside the profession. To psychologists a 'pervert' is someone suffering from a psycho-sexual disorder but to a non-psychologist it means a morally despised, much hated person. Most people in a trade – whether it's illegal like burglary, semi-illegal like prostitution, or totally above-board like the medical profession – use a vocabulary which can be difficult for outsiders to understand. Someone with a discharge from their vagina or penis might be alarmed to hear a doctor diagnose '*Candida albicans*', but reassured when they hear that all they've got is 'thrush'.

lexicographer This is someone who writes or compiles a dictionary. The great eighteenth-century lexicographer Samuel Johnson defined the word as 'a harmless drudge'. Lexicographers aren't always very brave: between 1791 and 1965 none of them dared print the word 'cunt' for fear of prosecution.

lingua franca Italian for 'Frankish language', originally the common vocabulary consisting of Italian mixed with French, Spanish, Greek, and Arabic spoken in Mediterranean ports. It has come to mean something that resembles a common language. Words and expressions like 'making out', 'going all the way' and 'petting' might be described as part of the lingua franca of teenagers today.

low A word that is coarse or VULGAR is often described as low. This usually refers to words used in spoken language (see COLLOQUIALISM) because most writers prefer to use words that aren't considered rude or offensive. This isn't true of bawdy, pornographic, or erotic literature. (See entries for these words in the main part of the book.)

metaphor A figure of speech (see FIGURATIVE) for an imaginative way of describing something by saying that it has the typical qualities of something else. The term 'to ride' meaning 'sexual intercourse' is a metaphor.

middle English This period in the history of the English language dates roughly from the twelfth century to the fifteenth century. Like the previous ANGLO-SAXON period, the English language during this time was greatly influenced by French and some Latin. (French was the official formal language of the Royal Court.) Geoffrey Chaucer is probably the most famous writer of this period.

modern English The period in the history of English from the sixteenth century to the present day. Latin, and to a lesser extent Greek, directly influenced the development of English at first and later other languages and dialects from all round the world – especially American English in the twentieth century. Two major influences on the English language in the early part of the modern period were Shakespeare and the invention of the printing press.

neologism A newly invented or COINED word from the Greek *neos* meaning 'new', and *logos* meaning 'word'. 'Hunk' meaning a sexually attractive, ruggedly masculine young man is a recent neologism that entered the language during the 1980s.

obsolescent A word that is going out of use. 'Slattern', meaning a scruffy, dirty, sexually promiscuous woman is currently obsolescent – it's still used but not as often as before, probably because 'slut' seems to say the same thing.

obsolete A word that is out of date and no longer used is called obsolete, from the Latin for 'worn out'. Some words disappear completely, others stay in use but a particular sense may stop being used. The word 'jade' used to mean a tired old prostitute; this sense is now obsolete but we still use 'jaded' to mean overworked or exhausted. 'Sard', perhaps the oldest English term for sexual intercourse, has been obsolete since around AD 950. Some words become obsolete and then come back into use again. This happened to 'glamour' (see entry in main part of this book).

Old English Another term for ANGLO-SAXON.

onomatopoeia The name for a type of word that sounds like the thing it represents. 'Pee' and 'piss' are both onomatopoeic words for 'urine' because of the sound that is made when someone is urinating.

prefix A short verbal term that goes immediately in front of a word. With a couple of different prefixes 'menorrhoea' meaning the menstrual flow can be turned into either 'amenorrhoea' meaning 'without periods', or 'dysmenorrhoea' meaning 'painful periods'.

PUN: A clever and usually amusing use of a word so that what you say has two different meanings. See also DOUBLE ENTENDRE.

racism Words themselves aren't racist (or sexist, ageist, etc) but the people who use them and the meanings they give them can be. In the nineteenth century 'a bit of grease' was apparently a humorous term for an Indian woman. But since a woman is a lot more than just a 'small piece', 'bit' was (and still is) widely used for a woman seen by men as a sex object, and 'grease' is nasty, smelly and slimy, it's hard not to come to the conclusion that although the individual words are perfectly harmless, it's a term that could only have been used by a white male racist.

rhyming slang Originally a secret ARGOT depending on rhyme as a device. It was first used at the beginning of the nineteenth century by cockney street-sellers (a Cockney is traditionally someone born within the sound of the bells from the church in Bow Street in London's East End), and by London small-time thieves and criminals. It spread to Australia by deported criminals where it picked up some Irish and New Zealand terms. Rhyming slang usually consists of two words with the last one rhyming with the word it means. The first word or first syllable of the first word is the one that gets spoken and this doesn't rhyme with the word it represents, making it totally baffling to someone who doesn't know the whole term. 'Berk' meaning a stupid or silly person, comes from 'Berkshire' or 'Berkeley Hunt', which is rhyming slang for 'cunt'.

Sanskrit An ancient language of India (one of the INDO-EUROPEAN family) now only used for religious purposes by Hindus. The English language has many words that originated in or were borrowed from Sanskrit. (See 'lingam' and 'yoni' in the main part of the book.)

semantics The study of word meanings. From the Greek for 'significant', which came from another Greek word meaning 'sign, token'.

sexism Because the English language has so many words which describe women or their sex organs in negative terms it's tempting to think that the words themselves must be sexist (i.e. they discriminate against women). But words themselves are neutral – it's human beings who give negative sexist meanings to certain words. The word 'cunt' was once STANDARD ENGLISH, but in the sixteenth century it became an abusive term for someone who was totally despised and hated. This wasn't the fault of the word but of the people who used it in this way.

simile A figure of speech (see FIGURATIVE) for an expression in which a person or thing is described as being similar to someone or something else. It's usually introduced by 'as' or 'like'. 'My love's like a red, red rose', from a poem by the Scottish poet Robert Burns is a good example of a simile.

slang A body of words and expressions frequently used and understood by a large number of people, but not accepted as good, formal language by the majority. A slang word is best defined by the person who uses it, where and when it's used and what 'flavour' it conveys. The informal vocabulary of slang is often made up of new words and meanings, extravagant picturesque figures of speech, impolite or vulgar references, etc. It belongs more to familiar conversation than to the written language. The origins of the word itself aren't known, although in northern British dialect 'slang' meant 'abusive language' and may be connected with the Norwegian dialect words *slengjenamn* meaning 'nickname', and *slengeord* meaning both 'offensive language' and 'new word introduced without special reason'.

Standard English The spoken and written English language that is understood and considered acceptable by the majority of educated English-speaking people. A word can have a Standard English use and a slang use at the same time – 'cherry' in Standard English is a fruit and a hymen in slang.

suffix From the Latin for 'to fix', this is a verbal term that goes at the end of a word. Common suffixes are '-ation', '-itis', '-fy' and '-ing'. A word with '-itis' as its suffix usually means 'inflammation of' as in 'tonsilitis', meaning inflammation of the tonsils.

synonym Two or more words that have the same meaning are known as synonyms. It's been estimated that there are over two hundred words all meaning a sexually promiscuous woman but only about twenty for a sexually promiscuous man. Some so-called synonyms may have slightly different shades of meaning or CONNOTATION: 'prostitute', 'whore' and 'harlot' all mean a woman who sells sex professionally but they're not exactly the same.

taboo A word which is avoided or prohibited by social custom. The word comes from *tabu*, a Polynesian word from the island of Tonga meaning the 'system or act of setting apart persons or things considered accursed or sacred'. Most taboo words in the English language are slang terms related to sex. Among the top taboo words today are 'cunt', 'motherfucker', 'fuck', 'cocksucker' and 'pussy'. Regardless of their length they're sometimes referred to as 'four-letter words'. (See also entry in main part of the book for further meanings of 'taboo'.)

vernacular The vernacular of a particular country or district is the language spoken most widely there. The word comes from the Latin *vernaculus* meaning 'belonging to a household slave', because slaves only spoke one language.

vulgar The vulgar tongue is the language spoken by the common people; it's another term for the VERNACULAR. A vulgarism is a word or expression that originated from, or is used chiefly by, illiterate people. A vulgar remark is one that's considered socially unacceptable or offensive. Vulgar comes from the Latin for 'mob' or 'the common people' – that is, those who couldn't read or write.